Parker kiss[illegible]’d been dying [illegible]s a pool of col[illegible]

How could he [illegible] for so long? Hadn’t anyone bothered to get to know the man—this caring, passionate man?

Only Abby had found the true Parker. She was in love with him.

He shouldn’t have kissed her. He was supposed to be dazzling her, not kissing her, but Parker couldn’t help himself.

He wasn’t used to having his feelings overrule his head. People who were ruled by their emotions got into trouble. Jay was a perfect example. But with any luck Jay had already forgotten about a certain temporary executive assistant.

Now all Parker had to do was to see that a certain temporary executive assistant forgot all about Jay.

Welcome to

Whirlwind Weddings is a brand-new mini-series about matrimony, featuring strong, irresistible heroes, feisty heroines and four marriages made not so much in heaven as in a hurry!

When the authors came up with the idea for **Whirlwind Weddings** we gave them just one stipulation: their heroes and heroines had to meet and marry within a week! Mission impossible? Well, a lot can happen in seven days…

Titles in this series are:

April	DASH TO THE ALTAR by Ruth Jean Dale
May	**MARRY IN HASTE by Heather Allison**
June	MARRIED IN A MOMENT by Jessica Steele
July	THE TWENTY-FOUR-HOUR BRIDE by Day Leclaire

Heather Allison says: 'My wedding was anything *but* whirlwind. After five years of dating, I married my high-school sweetheart on the fourth of July in Houston, Texas. I still can't believe my mother didn't talk me out of an outdoor reception. It was July, for pity's sake! Even the cake was sweating. But when we saw the fireworks display we forgot all about the heat, humidity, and mosquitoes—we must have, because every year we're right back outside watching for fireworks on the fourth.'

MARRY IN HASTE

BY

HEATHER ALLISON

In memory of Megan Alyssa Fox,
who is only gone from our sight.

First published in Great Britain 1998
Harlequin Mills & Boon Limited,
Eton House, 18-24 Paradise Road, Richmond, Surrey TW9 1SR

ISBN 0 263 80767 3

Set in Times Roman 11 on 11½ pt.
02-9805-45982 C1

Printed and bound in Great Britain
by Mackays of Chatham PLC, Chatham

CHAPTER ONE

"ABIGAIL? Could you come into my office?"

Slipping her feet into her pumps, Abby Monroe stood and smoothed the skirt of her suit. Pausing to pick up the notebook and pen she always kept ready on her desk, she walked across the plush terracotta and jade diamond-patterned carpet and into the office of the Executive Assistant to Parker Laird, of Laird Drilling and Exploration.

Abby loved the carpet, with its deep pile and thick pad that put a spring into her step. In fact, she loved everything about working on the twenty-sixth floor of the Laird building.

As she'd climbed the corporate ladder during the past four years, Abby had discovered that the more important the person she worked for, the higher the floor and the thicker the carpet.

This was the top floor and the carpet was so thick, if it were any thicker, the doors wouldn't slide over it.

Even the atmosphere was different than it was on the lower floors. This was the nerve center of the whole company and power hummed through the air, generated by Parker Laird, himself.

Valerie Chippin, the Executive Assistant and Abby's boss as of five weeks ago, closed the door and waved Abby over to the sitting area by the corner windows.

This was unusual. Abby hadn't ever been invited to sit on the jade leather chairs and love seat before.

As she followed Valerie, Abby admired the view from the spacious corner office.

Someday, *she* would have an office like this, with all of Houston, Texas—or someplace else—at her feet.

But that was some other day and not today.

She sat in the chair across from Valerie and crossed her feet at the ankles.

"I've been very pleased with your work the past several weeks," Valerie began.

Abby covered her surprise with a smile. Valerie wasn't one to compliment her staff's performance, yet Abby had continued to work hard, just as she'd always done.

"And so has Mr. Laird," Valerie added diplomatically.

Abby maintained her smile, though she was certain Parker Laird didn't have a clue that she existed. Oh, he nodded, if he happened to catch her eye as he stepped off the elevator, but more often than not, he was reading the *Wall Street Journal* and continued to do so as he entered his office, which took up half the twenty-sixth floor.

Abby's desk was positioned opposite the elevator where she was the first person people saw. It was her job to act as receptionist, in addition to her other duties. Though receptionist duty was a step down from the secretary she'd been, Abby didn't really mind, recognizing that she was the least experienced member of Valerie's staff.

But she wouldn't always be.

"As you know, I'm going on vacation next week," Valerie continued.

Expecting some long-term assignments, Abby opened her notebook, but Valerie shook her head.

''Not yet.'' She drew a breath. ''It's an awkward time for me to leave, I know, since Laird is establishing drilling operations in the El Bahar oil field, but my husband booked this cruise a year ago.'' She smiled and patted her perfectly coiffed blond head.

Abby mentally compared the sleek style with her own naturally curly auburn hair and sighed inwardly, longing for the professionalism of tamable hair.

''It's our twenty-fifth wedding anniversary,'' Valerie confided.

''Congratulations,'' Abby replied automatically, stunned that Valerie was even discussing the subject with her.

Valerie rarely referred to her personal life. Rumor had it she didn't have one, and Abby could believe it. No matter how early Abby arrived, or how late she stayed, Valerie worked longer.

And so did Parker Laird.

In fact, attached to his office was a bedroom, bath and kitchenette, though why he'd want to spend the night in the Laird building when he owned a fabulous house in the River Oaks area of Houston, Abby didn't know.

''Mr. Laird has graciously insisted that my husband and I go on our cruise.'' Valerie seemed to believe it was important that Abby not think she was shirking her duty to Parker Laird. ''I'll be gone for a month.''

''A month?'' Abby blurted out before she thought better of it.

''Yes.'' Valerie's lips tightened.

Abby recovered. ''I'll certainly do my best to support...'' Support whom? Which of the two other staffers would take Valerie's place? ''To provide all the support I can,'' she amended.

''That's what I wanted to discuss with you.

Abigail…'' Valerie visibly hesitated. ''I've recommended to Mr. Laird that you be his assistant while I'm away.''

''You recommended *me*?'' Her voice cracked on the last word. As she spoke, Abby knew she should be acting confident and professional, thus reassuring Valerie that she'd made the right decision. But to be named Acting Executive Assistant to Parker Laird…

''You're surprised.'' A knowing smile curved Valerie's lips.

Shocked was a better description, but Abby tried to pretend she wasn't. ''I'm delighted for the opportunity—''

''But you're wondering at your good fortune?'' Valerie spoke dryly and laced her fingers over her knees.

Abby kept quiet. Valerie wouldn't be fooled by denials and Abby shouldn't embarrass herself by trying to bluff.

''Barbara and Nancy have been on my staff much longer, but Barbara has two young children and Nancy has a boyfriend who isn't quite as understanding about irregular hours as my husband, Gordon, is. I don't believe you have a boyfriend?''

Abby shook her head.

''Family obligations?''

Again, Abby shook her head.

''That's best. Mr. Laird requires someone to be on call virtually twenty-four hours a day.'' Valerie sighed faintly. ''Sometimes I think Laird Drilling has an operation in every time zone in the world. The person who fills in for me will have to be flexible—''

''And I am!'' Abby would tie herself into knots for an opportunity like this one.

"—and a hard worker. You'll also have to be decisive, and if you can read minds, that will help."

Abby chuckled politely, but she had a feeling Valerie was half serious.

"We have a week before I leave. I'll show you my files so you can become familiar with the way Mr. Laird likes things done." Valerie stood and so did Abby. "We'll meet with him after he returns from the Chamber of Commerce luncheon."

Valerie strode across the office followed by a dazed Abby. "Until then, this is the Laird executive directory. You should familiarize yourself with the names and pictures so you'll know who Mr. Laird deals with most frequently." Valerie held out a thick paperback book.

Abby took the directory, though she'd already spent several lunch hours studying it in an effort to become more efficient. It appeared her initiative had paid off—and far more quickly than she'd ever imagined. "Thank you, Ms. Chippin. I appreciate your confidence in me and I won't let you down."

"I'm counting on that, Abigail. See you at one-thirty."

As Valerie spoke, a dark blur passed the doorway. "Hang on. Looks like you're about to get your first lesson in flexibility," she murmured.

Within seconds the intercom on Valerie's desk sounded. "Valerie? I can see you now."

"On my way, Mr. Laird." Valerie raised her eyebrows. "You see? He's back forty-five minutes early and expects me to be ready and available for the meeting I requested."

Hands quivering, Abby nodded and scribbled an illegible note in her pad. She mustn't let on how nervous she was or Parker Laird would reject her as an assistant for sure.

Beckoning to her, Valerie opened the door connecting her office to the conference room and led Abby through it. A door on the other side opened into Parker's office.

''When you bring people for a meeting, you'll take them in the other door, of course.''

''Certainly,'' Abby murmured, able to figure that out for herself. Nevertheless, she made a note, mostly to see if her fingers were working properly yet.

And then Valerie was opening the door to Parker Laird's office.

Abby held her breath as the bottom of the door whispered across the carpet.

Parker Laird stood facing the windows behind his desk, dictating into a small personal tape recorder. He glanced toward them, but continued talking, his eyes watching Abby as she followed Valerie.

Abby didn't know where to look, so she met his unnerving gray gaze. That he could study her so thoroughly, yet still focus on what he was saying, demonstrated just how he was single-handedly able to run a company the size of Laird Drilling.

He was young for such a position, but everyone knew that. And with his dark wavy hair and black eyebrows, he was incredibly handsome—Abby already knew that, too. But according to the gossips, all that handsomeness was wasted, since Parker Laird was already married—to his company. They even said that when he was cut, he bled oil.

Before now, the most Abby had ever seen of Parker Laird was when he was either coming from or going to somewhere. He walked very fast, his long strides making it difficult for people to keep up with him. It amused her to see him emerge from the elevator and take off down the hall, followed by men who huffed and puffed and still tried to talk with him. He didn't walk that fast with Valerie, but even so, Abby had seen her jog a step or two at times.

Valerie headed toward two armless chairs positioned at the end of Parker's desk and indicated that Abby should sit in one. Valerie reached under the edge of the massive desk and pulled out an extension ledge that sprang into place. On it, she set her enormous planning book opened to a calendar, and a small tape recorder like the one Parker was using. Then she waited.

Abby took a deep breath, grateful for the few minutes to compose herself, though with Parker Laird only a few feet away from her, how could she?

She was in Parker Laird's inner sanctum, actually breathing the same air. Abby inhaled again. There *was* something different about the air in here, something that accounted for the charge in the atmosphere. Abby wondered about the man responsible for it.

He'd turned back to the windows, so she studied him, allowing her gaze to roam over his perfectly chiseled profile, perfectly tailored suit and perfectly shined shoes. Obviously, nothing less than perfection would do for Parker Laird.

She waited, ready to attempt perfection.

The minutes passed. He wasn't one to waste time, but as Abby sat there, waiting for him to finish whatever it was he was doing, she became impatient. She was in the middle of several projects which she would have to complete before taking over for Valerie.

And she was missing her lunch.

He launched into another set of comments and

Abby rolled her eyes and grimaced. Couldn't he have waited until after he was finished to call them in here?

At that moment, her eyes met his in the reflection of the window.

He'd been watching her and she hadn't known it. Abby swallowed, her mouth suddenly dry. From now on, when she was called into his office, she would bring an extra task with her. And if she didn't have anything, she'd make something up.

Parker turned then and set the recorder on his desk. "Sorry to keep you waiting, ladies."

He'd seen her expression. As her cheeks warmed, Abby heard Valerie introduce her.

"Mr. Laird, as we discussed, Abigail Monroe will be filling in for me while I'm away."

They'd met previously, of course, but Abby knew that before, she was only one of hundreds of faceless employees.

"Thanks for helping us out here, Abigail." Parker reached down to shake her hand.

"Please call me Abby," she said impulsively when it became apparent that he wasn't going to hold her impatience against her. His hand closed over hers, his grip firm without being overpowering. It was a confident grip, accompanied by a brief smile.

Abby hadn't seen him smile much and was struck by the warmth in it.

"And how's school going, Abby?" he asked, sitting in his desk chair and swiveling it to face her.

Abby caught a movement on her left as Valerie jerked her head to stare at her. Valerie obviously hadn't known Abby was studying to get her business degree, making it even more astonishing that Parker had.

"F-fine." When Valerie had asked about obligations, Abby hadn't mentioned her night classes. ''I have my final exam this week, and then the spring term will be over.'' She understood that nothing could interfere with her duties to Parker Laird.

He hadn't missed Valerie's look of surprise. ''I believe Abby is taking advantage of our tuition reimbursement program,'' he said to Valerie.

''I'd forgotten that,'' she murmured.

''What are you studying?'' Parker asked. As he spoke, he removed the tape from the recorder and handed it to Valerie, who wrote on the label.

''Business Administration,'' Abby answered, conscious that Valerie was less than pleased with her.

Parker nodded, then swiveled back around, obviously finished with the small talk. ''Schedule for this afternoon?''

Turning on her recorder, Valerie instantly began reading appointments from her book which Parker either confirmed, or amended, then added comments.

They spoke in a rapid shorthand that Abby could barely follow. Parker's day was scheduled in fifteen-minute blocks until ten o'clock at night and, sometimes, he was doing more than one activity during a block.

He returned phone calls while exercising on the treadmill. He met with people during meals. He dictated during his commute.

The man apparently never took a break. It wouldn't surprise Abby to know that he listened to self-help tapes in his sleep.

She, who worked full-time and went to school at night, felt like a slug in comparison.

''Abby, when do your classes meet?'' he asked.

The question surprised her. ''I'm just taking one

this semester. It meets Tuesday and Thursday nights from seven until ten.''

Incredibly, Valerie was marking it on the master schedule.

''And your final exam?''

''This Thursday.''

''Block out Wednesday evening as well, Valerie,'' Parker instructed. ''She'll need to study.''

Abby was both stunned and touched that a man who regularly functioned on a global scale would even think of such minute details—or care.

Perhaps that was his secret: think big, but don't forget little. She was going to learn a lot in the month ahead.

For the next ten minutes, Abby listened to more rapid-fire directions and updates and wondered how on earth she would ever keep up.

''That's enough for now.'' Parker pulled his cuff back and glanced at his watch. ''Let Abby update the schedule and then she can work with you this afternoon.''

A look passed between Parker and Valerie.

''Go ahead and get started on the schedule,'' she said, closed the calendar and passed it and the tape to Abby. ''The name of the computer file is printed at the bottom.''

Abby stacked the book with the directory and stood. They were going to talk about her, she knew. ''Shall I transcribe the tape as well?''

Valerie nodded, and Abby walked briskly from the room.

''She's very young,'' Parker commented as he watched Abby's retreat, then leveled his gaze at the woman who'd been his father's Executive Assistant and then his when he'd become CEO of Laird Drilling after his father had died. "Interesting choice."

"Abigail Monroe is bright and a hard worker."

"I've read her performance reviews." Parker tapped a file folder on his desk. "But she's only been on staff, what, six weeks?"

Valerie shifted. "That's true, however, I feel she'll have more flexibility than Barbara or Nancy."

"Flexibility is important." Parker smiled inwardly. Valerie had been able to meet his eyes as she spoke, he'd give her credit for that.

He knew exactly what she was doing by leaving an inexperienced substitute in her place while she was gone, and under other circumstances, he wouldn't allow it.

But these were not normal circumstances. The strongest quality little Abby Monroe had going for her was a freckle-faced, farm girl unsophistication that wouldn't appeal to his brother, Jay.

Valerie must have been thinking along the same line. "Should I brief her on all the...unique aspects of the El Bahar project?"

"You can stress how important it is that Jay not be distracted in any way from his preparations to head up that operation." Parker smiled grimly. "And I'll make sure there are plenty of preparations to keep him occupied until the minute his plane leaves the ground."

"Oh, Mr. Laird!" Valerie gripped her hands. "I shouldn't be abandoning you now, of all times!"

"You don't have a choice." Reaching across his desk, Parker plucked an envelope containing two first-class airline tickets from his blotter. He'd also upgraded their stateroom to a suite. "In all the years you've worked for me, Gordon has never complained about missed dinners and holiday crises. If you canceled his cruise, he'd never forgive either of us.'' He slid the envelope over to her. ''Happy anniversary.''

''Mr. Laird!'' Valerie swallowed, obviously preparing to gush her thanks.

Parker forestalled her with an upheld hand. ''Have a good time.''

Abby concentrated on keeping her knees from wobbling as she made her way over the thick carpeting and back to her desk.

She was going to be Parker Laird's Executive Assistant!

Mentally, she repeated this astonishing fact until her breathing slowed and she could think once more. Reaching her desk, she dumped everything onto it, then allowed her knees to give way as she sank onto her chair.

Hello, I'm Abigail Monroe, acting as Parker Laird's Executive Assistant while Ms. Chippin is away. Mr. Laird will be entertaining a party of five Thursday evening at eight-thirty.

This is Abby Monroe, Parker Laird's Executive Assistant. Please reserve the Presidential suite for Mr. Laird.

This is Abby Monroe...yes, that's right. Parker Laird's Executive Assistant...

How many times had she imagined saying those words or a variation? Becoming an Executive Assistant had been Abby's goal ever since she'd started working at Laird Drilling and Exploration.

She hadn't realized such a position existed until she'd listened to the office talk and then it seemed like a perfect job. Excitement, travel, responsibility, meeting famous people—that's the kind of life Valerie Chippin had.

She rode in a limousine with a driver, attended luncheons at fancy restaurants with fancy foods, wore designer suits and traveled to exotic destinations. Valerie Chippin lived the way Abby had dreamed of back when she was growing up in the tiny town of Haste, Texas.

When Abby had been promoted to Valerie's staff just weeks ago, she'd been thrilled, thinking her hard work was paying off.

And now this.

Abby stole a glance into Nancy and Barbara's office. The two women were at lunch and Abby wondered if Valerie had told them the news yet.

Probably not. Abby doubted they would have been so calm. In fact, Abby didn't want to be here when they were told the news.

It wasn't that she didn't get along with Nancy and Barbara, it was just that the two women had worked together for several years and Abby was the junior newcomer. Abby got the routine and less interesting work. Lunchtimes were staggered so someone was always available to answer the telephones, but Nancy and Barbara always went to lunch together and Abby went later, by herself.

She didn't mind. She accepted the fact that she was the least senior of the group.

Until a few moments ago.

Abby checked her watch. No time for lunch today, though she was so excited she wouldn't have been able to eat.

She immediately started work updating the schedule and was transcribing the tape when at ten after one, Nancy and Barbara returned. They were late, Abby noted, and they'd left five minutes early.

They probably thought no one had noticed, but now Abby knew that Valerie must have. Abby never left early and was never late. In fact, it was rare for her to take the full hour allotted to her.

Abby could hear the women talking in the office they shared. Through the fogged glass, she could see that Valerie was back in her office. She had to tell them Abby's new position soon.

Sure enough, she heard Valerie's voice on the intercom.

Feeling cowardly, Abby grabbed her purse and slipped away from her desk. She took the stairs to the floor below and headed toward the vending machines.

She should eat something so she would be sharp this afternoon, but her stomach rebelled at the thought of food. Abby settled for a plastic container of orange juice though she had to force herself to drink it.

No one else was in the tiny snack bar so Abby closed her eyes and took several deep breaths, trying not to think about the fact that she was about to embark upon the greatest opportunity of her career.

Even though it was only for a month, Abby would forever after be able to say on her résumé that she had worked as Acting Executive Assistant to Parker Laird, CEO of Laird Drilling and Exploration.

She would be an *experienced* Executive Assistant.

Abby threw away the empty orange juice container, then stopped by the ladies' room to touch up her makeup and comb her hair.

She heard the voices even before she pushed open the door to the outer sitting area.

"I heard what she said, but I still don't understand!" Nancy's angry voice bounced off the tiled floor and walls of the rest room area. "One of us should be in charge while she's gone, not *Abby*."

Abby froze.

"Oh, it makes perfect sense." Barbara's voice was moderated.

"Yeah, right. You've been here six years, I've been here three, and Abby's got less than two months under her belt. *Perfect* sense."

"It's not worth getting angry over."

"Maybe you don't mind spending the rest of your working career as a secretary to a glorified girl Friday, but I want to know that someday, I can aspire to be...that girl Friday!"

Barbara laughed. "Then pay attention. How many times has Valerie gone on vacation?"

"She never goes on vacation."

"Right. And now she's going to be gone for an entire month, a month in which Parker Laird will discover how much he depends on her because things are not going to run smoothly with Abby in charge."

"Which is why one of *us* should be in charge."

"Which is why one of us is *not* in charge."

There was a silence.

Abby tried to understand what Barbara was saying, but couldn't.

Nancy apparently couldn't, either. "I don't get it."

"Valerie wants to have a job when she gets back—her well-paid, perk-laden job. She's got Parker thinking she's indispensable. If either of us took her place, Parker would discover that we can do the job just as well as she can, but Abby will mess up so much, Parker Laird will be thrilled when Valerie comes back."

"She is so smart!" Nancy said, awe in her voice. "I'm going to remember this."

And so would she, Abby vowed and slipped out of the rest room.

So she was expected to fail.

Well, then she wouldn't. Abby climbed the stairs back to the twenty-sixth floor. She'd prove everyone wrong. She could do this job, she knew it.

Now all she had to do was prove it to Parker Laird.

CHAPTER TWO

THE following Monday, Abby arrived on the twenty-sixth floor at seven o'clock in the morning. She was armed with pieces of paper on which she'd scribbled the last-minute instructions Valerie had telephoned from the airport in Houston and astonishingly, again from Athens, waking Abby up in the middle of the night.

Quite frankly, Abby hadn't relaxed until she'd called the cruise line to see if the ship had sailed. Even then, it wouldn't surprise her if Valerie managed a ship-to-shore call.

Abby automatically sat at her own desk, then smiled when she remembered she was entitled to use Valerie's office for the next month. Nancy and Barbara would be sharing receptionist duty. While she transferred her nameplate, calendar and glass paperweight from her desk to Valerie's, Abby made a mental note to inform Mr. Laird of their schedule.

Arms full, she fumbled with the key to Valerie's office door, the scratching sounds loud in the silence. Though always quiet, the twenty-sixth floor seemed eerie just because Abby knew she was alone.

The first thing she did after dumping her armload on the desk was to put Valerie's nameplate in the drawer and replace it with her own. Abby had invested in the heavy etched glass because the design looked substantial, yet feminine, and more important than the brown plastic plates Laird issued to its employees. Beside it, she set the matching calendar.

The paperweight, though also of a heavy glass, wasn't part of the set. Floating in the oval were foreign canceled stamps, reminding Abby of the places she could travel if she kept working toward her goal. She set the paperweight by the computer monitor.

Before she started to work, Abby drew the blinds all the way to the top of the windows and stared across the city of Houston. An orange sun burned through the exhaust haze as rush-hour traffic clogged the freeways.

No one in her family could understand the appeal of the big city to Abby. ''Full of people, noise, traffic and pollution,'' they said.

But Abby felt the excitement and energy—she'd yield on the pollution.

The city—this building—was where things happened and now Abby was an important part of it all.

Or she would be as soon as she figured out what to do next. Sorting through her notes, Abby shook her head. For a week, she'd been Valerie's shadow and the recipient of volumes of minutiae, yet she wasn't as secure in her knowledge of the routines as she'd like to be. It seemed that no day was a typical day, and Valerie kept entirely too much information in her head. She dispensed pieces of information out of context and whenever she remembered.

Abby decided that she'd start an instruction journal for the next time someone had to fill in as Executive Assistant.

She spent several minutes transferring notes into the master schedule, an oversized portfolio, and tossing snippets of paper before discovering a lump underneath the bottom layer.

A cassette tape. Mr. Laird's cassette tape. It had

probably been on Valerie's desk when Abby dumped the papers onto it.

Popping the tape into the machine, she put on the headphones.

"Good morning, Abby." Parker Laird's deep voice sounded in her ears. "Please make the following schedule changes and have a revised copy on my desk as soon as possible."

As Abby listened to the instructions, she was dismayed to realize that Parker had made the tape *this* morning, prior to her early arrival.

Did the man never sleep?

Abby concentrated on Parker's rapid-fire instructions. Although in deference to her inexperience, he frequently elaborated on what he wanted and who the members of various groups were, Abby had to rewind the tape countless times. She had a headache before eight o'clock. She also had several hours' work ahead of her and hadn't yet made a copy of the receptionist schedule.

But of course, she reminded herself, that's why the Executive Assistant had a staff. She opened the door connecting Valerie's office with Barbara and Nancy's and stopped.

The office was empty. It was also ten past eight.

Her intercom buzzed. "Abby?"

Parker. Abby leaped to answer it. "Yes, Mr. Laird?"

"You didn't leave a message, so I didn't know if you were in or not."

There hadn't been anything on the tape about a message. "I've been here over an hour."

"I wish I'd known. I've been waiting for you."

There was no censure in his voice, yet even alone in the office, Abby's face heated. "I'll be right there."

She fanned her face and started for Mr. Laird's office, then stopped. With Nancy and Barbara not in yet, there was no one to answer the telephone. And Abby hadn't had a chance to print out Mr. Laird's revised schedule.

Scribbling some instructions on a sticky note, Abby stuck it right in the center of Barbara's computer monitor, then hurried into Mr. Laird's office.

What a horrible start to her tenure as his Executive Assistant.

Breathless, she arrived at the center of power without noticing the air, the carpet or the view.

But she did notice Parker Laird.

He stood clear on the other side of the room behind a long table covered with maps. Without looking at her, he beckoned her forward with the barest movement of his fingers.

Abby didn't know whether she was supposed to join him at the table, or take the usual spot at the end of his desk. Valerie always seemed to know, but Abby couldn't tell how. She hovered uncertainly by the desk.

Parker pulled a swing-arm lamp closer to the map. "Did you forget to tell me you were in this morning?"

"There weren't any instructions to do so on the tape you left."

He didn't respond and Abby just stayed quiet. He still hadn't looked at her. At last, he straightened, tapped the map with his finger, stared some more, then abruptly wheeled around and strode over to his desk. "From now on, when you arrive, leave a message on my voice mail."

"Yes, Mr. Laird." Abby made a note. This was a

routine Valerie hadn't told her about. She hoped the oversight wasn't on purpose, but suspected it was.

"Do you have a copy of the revised schedule?" Parker Laird, all white shirt and French cuffs, sat at the desk and swiveled to face her.

"I was working on it when you called. I left instructions for Barbara to print out a copy."

Parker looked down at his watch and then at her. "And that will be...?"

Abby swallowed, torn between defending herself by exposing Barbara and Nancy, thus completely alienating them, or taking the blame for not being organized this morning. "As soon as possible, Mr. Laird," she bluffed and met his gaze, pen poised.

He continued to gaze at her, his expression attentively blank, as though waiting for her to grasp some concept. She had a horrible feeling that he wasn't fooled at all.

"Do you have any further changes to the schedule before we print out a final copy?" she asked, mostly to sound efficient in spite of her inefficiency.

"There's never a final copy," he murmured. "Only a most recent copy."

"Do you have any further changes to the schedule before we print out the most recent copy?" Abby amended as though she hadn't previously spoken.

Parker Laird blinked. He was looking at her as though he was inwardly amused and teetering on the edge of a smile.

"Coffee?" he asked.

"No, thank you, Mr. Laird."

He continued to gaze at her with the same expression.

"Oh!" Abby shot to her feet. "Coffee!" *No, thank you, Mr. Laird.* She cringed. "I—I'll—"

He held up a hand. ''Making coffee isn't one of your responsibilities, but if you happen to be drinking a cup when I call for you, feel free to bring it with you.''

''Of course, Mr. Laird.'' Abby was a tea drinker but couldn't imagine ever being relaxed enough to drink in front of Parker Laird.

''In fact, should you want a cup, say, right now, you can get one when you bring the schedule.'' He spoke in a measured tone with only the slightest emphasis on the last words.

Bring the schedule. Abby got the message. ''Thank you, Mr. Laird.'' Abby backed her way across the room. ''That's very thoughtful of you.''

Idiot, idiot, idiot, she chanted to herself as she raced back to her office.

Incredibly, neither Barbara nor Nancy had arrived. Abby sat at the computer, frantically opened the schedule file and typed in the changes, conscious of the passing minutes—conscious that the current fifteen minute block of time was allocated to ''Phone Ian Douglass in Aberdeen'' and not ''Wait for Abby to type schedule.''

She was shouting, ''Hurry!'' at the laser printer when Barbara arrived, a cup from a gourmet coffee shop in her hand.

''A little frazzled this morning, are we?'' she asked.

''Where have you been?'' Abby snapped. She'd rehearsed various approaches at chastising Barbara and Nancy for their tardiness. This wasn't one of them.

''Valerie told us to come in at eight-thirty this morning. She thought it would give you time to get organized.''

Abby yanked the pages from the printer output. ''From now on, please come in at eight o'clock. Even earlier, if you can manage.'' She was so angry, she could barely look at Barbara.

''I'll try, but it depends on traffic and the school won't let parents drop off their kids before seven-thirty.''

At that, Abby looked fully at Barbara. ''I was here at seven this morning,'' she said evenly, ''and there was an entire tape of instructions waiting for me.'' *Now do you see why Valerie named me Acting Executive Assistant*?

Barbara apparently received Abby's unspoken message. ''What can I do?'' she asked, stuffing her purse in the bottom drawer of her desk.

''I'm on my way back to Mr. Laird's office. He has a meeting at ten and wants files pulled to study before then. Details are in my notes.''

Barbara pried the plastic cover off her coffee cup. ''I'll take care of it.''

Glad the challenge to her authority had come and gone quickly, Abby hurried back to Parker's office. Outside, she drew several deep breaths so she wouldn't arrive panting at his desk.

Parker was facing the windows as he spoke on the phone when Abby unobtrusively took her seat by the desk.

''Yes, Ian.''

This would be the eight-thirty call to Aberdeen. Abby remembered her vow to have something to occupy herself. Of course, she didn't, so she studied the schedule, breaking down the tasks and assigning them to either Barbara or Nancy. She finished in three minutes, but pretended she hadn't.

She would *not* look in the glass.

As she worked, her skin prickled. *He's looking at me.*

But that was ridiculous. He wasn't *looking* looking. He was probably simply staring blankly as he concentrated on his telephone call.

From her experience with Valerie this past week, Abby had learned that Parker liked to jot notes immediately after a telephone call, so when he disconnected the call, she remained quiet.

He scribbled a line or two, then looked toward her with a raised eyebrow.

She stood. "Here's the schedule, Mr. Laird."

"Call me Parker, Abby," he said, taking it from her.

Call him *Parker*? Abby's mouth worked, but nothing came out.

He glanced up at her.

"A-all right, Mr. Laird."

"Parker."

"All right, Mr. Parker."

He blinked once, then said, "When you call me Parker, you get to drop the Mr."

"Yes, sir."

His brow furrowed. "It bothers you to use my name?"

Bother wasn't the right word. Maybe *uncomfortable* was, but she didn't want to admit to it. "Valerie always calls you Mr. Laird, so I'm used to it."

He nodded. "Valerie has called me Mr. Laird since I was thirteen years old. I cannot break her of the habit. If it helps, think of Parker as a more efficient use of time. Only two syllables to say."

Was he making a joke? "Yes, sir."

He gave her a long look before saying dryly, "*Sir* would, of course, be most efficient of all." Turning his attention to the schedule she'd set on his desk, he glanced through it. "The meeting at ten is informal and I don't anticipate it lasting more than an hour. However—'' he stopped and made a note ''—my brother will be with us, and Jay is notoriously unpredictable, so we might stretch to lunch. I want you to be prepared to order sandwiches—that sort of thing. Valerie uses the deli down the street.'' He waved his hand. ''They make an assortment platter that's worked well in the past.''

Abby knew what he was talking about. She'd called in the order before. ''Yes, sir—Parker.''

''Abby?''

She looked up and met his gray gaze.

''Parker,'' he murmured. ''Just Parker.''

Nodding, she repeated, ''Just Parker.'' *Parker, Parker, Parker*, she drilled into her mind. What was the matter with her? By asking her to call him Parker, he was trying to put her at ease and she'd turned it into something awkward instead of just calling him by his name.

During the next ten minutes, Abby avoided calling him anything at all. ''I'll be back with the files,'' she informed him when they'd finished, but he'd already turned his attention to the next event on his schedule.

Fortunately, Barbara had put the files he wanted on her desk. By the time Abby delivered them, Nancy had arrived and both women were ready for their next assignments. Abby showed them the schedule and the tasks, and without complaint or comment, they started working.

She sat down to catch her breath. She was refastening the barrette that clipped the hair at the back of her neck when the interoffice messenger wheeled in a dolly with two black boxes containing the morning's correspondence, reports, messages, requests and memos.

It was the Executive Assistant's job to sort through everything and decide what deserved Mr. Laird's—Parker's—personal attention and what could be handled by the staff.

She'd just reached for the brown routing envelope on top when the staff telephone started ringing. With resignation, she waited for the buzz on her phone.

Without a doubt, this first phone call would be some earth-shattering problem that she was ill-equipped to deal with. She dropped her head to her desk, and when the phone buzzed, it sounded loud in her ear.

''Peter Frostwood on line one,'' intoned Nancy. She'd drawn first receptionist duty.

Peter Frostwood was the head of Laird North America. Of course. Hadn't she expected as much?

''Abigail Monroe,'' she said.

There was a brief silence. ''I asked for Valerie.''

''I'm Acting Executive Assistant while Ms. Chippin is away,'' Abby reminded him. There had been a memo sent to all department heads. She'd typed it herself.

''Tell Parker I need to see him ASAP.''

This was where it got tricky. Abby had to decide, without knowing if Peter Frostwood was the alarmist type, whether to interrupt Parker's preparations for the meeting or give him the message at their noontime conference. Asking a highly-placed executive to explain himself was presumptuous. Interrupting Parker for every little thing defeated the whole purpose of an executive assistant.

''Mr. Laird is preparing for a meeting at ten o'clock and his schedule for the day is booked,'' she explained. ''Shall I put you through to discuss a time when it will be convenient for you to see him?''

"Yeah, go ahead."

Abby buzzed Parker. If he objected to the interruption, he'd tell her. "Peter Frostwood needs to speak with you."

"Okay."

And that was all. She'd chosen correctly. This time.

Abby eyed the two full boxes. She'd gone through similar boxes with Valerie last week and knew there would be another load delivered in the afternoon.

As Valerie had taught her, Abby culled the papers into those requiring action, signature, and information. Valerie ranked the action items, but Abby didn't feel capable yet. The production reports, long tedious pages of numbers, were to be entered into a spreadsheet program. That had frequently been Abby's job and she was delighted to assign it to Nancy.

The phone continued to ring and Abby found herself falling behind.

She still had to prepare for the meeting and at nine-thirty, went in to set up the conference room.

Setting up for a morning conference meant making coffee. Though she didn't drink the stuff herself, Abby had watched Valerie.

Parker Laird didn't settle for the prepackaged stuff, oh no. Valerie had rattled off the names of the beans in his custom mix, along with the fact that he liked them roasted a precise number of seconds and freshly ground.

To Abby, a coffee bean was a coffee bean. She poured them into the grinder, then dumped the grounds into a metallic-filtered basket, added tap water and hoped for the best.

The rest of the tray would be just as complicated as Parker Laird, himself. No powdered packets of coffee creamer and no plastic cups. That would be too easy, Abby grumbled to herself. There must be skim milk, cream and regular milk. Parker served both natural sugar and white sugar, along with two kinds of artificial sweetener. The coffee would be poured into heavy royal-blue mugs with the Laird Drilling and Exploration logo in white.

By the time Abby had made a pot of decaf and had carried in the tray, it was only ten minutes until the meeting should start. Feeling rushed and flustered, she bent down and yanked open the credenza doors to look for the napkins bearing the Laird logo. These were white, with the logo in royal blue.

"Hellooo, Valerie, my love. Have you decided to leave your husband and come away with me yet?"

Eyes wide, Abby jerked upright. Leaning against the conference room doorway was a younger version of Parker. This was the wickedly charming black sheep, Jay Laird, himself. Abby had only seen the back of his head before in person, since he was rarely here.

He was as handsome as everyone said he was with the gray Laird eyes and black hair. His skin was attractively tanned and his features weren't as sharply defined as Parker's.

"You're not Valerie."

Abby shook her head.

He advanced into the room, interest in his gray eyes, a winsome smile on his lips. "Come away with me anyway."

"I—I can't do that." She closed the cabinet doors. "I haven't finished setting up for the meeting."

He looked around the room. "Chairs, table…what more do we need?"

"Water," Abby said.

"Ah." Shoving his hands into the pockets of his

khaki trousers, he cocked his head sideways. ''If I fetch the water, can we sneak away?''

Abby smiled in spite of herself. ''Mr. Laird, you're supposed to be at this meeting.''

He winced. ''Jay, please.''

''Jay,'' she repeated easily.

He regarded her, his eyes crinkling at the corners. ''You know who I am.''

''Everyone knows who you are.''

''But I, alas, do not know who everyone is.''

Abby abandoned the microscopic hope that he might have noticed her sometime during the past four years. ''I'm Abby Monroe. Ms. Chippin is on a cruise and I'm filling in for her.''

''A cruise.'' He looked skyward. ''She left without me.'' He met her eyes with a soulful gaze. ''I'm devastated.''

Abby laughed, feeling the tension of the morning melt away for the first time.

''So, you've drawn the short straw.'' He tucked her hand through his arm. ''Come tell Uncle Jay all about it.''

''About what?'' With a smile, Abby disengaged her arm and picked up two empty water pitchers.

''About slaving for my brother. Do you have a life left?'' Jay followed her into the tiny coffee bar.

There was hardly room for one person, let alone two, and Abby was aware that he was standing close behind her as she filled the pitchers with ice and water. ''This is only my first day.''

''Quick!'' He grasped her shoulders. ''Run! Flee! Get out while you still can.''

Chuckling, Abby handed him a pitcher. ''I'm not afraid of hard work.''

''There's work and there's the rest of your life.''

Jay carried the pitcher into the conference area. ''My brother and I differ on how much time one should devote to each. You see, I work to live. Parker lives to work.''

It wasn't her place to comment, though Abby thought fleetingly of the pictures of a smiling Jay that regularly appeared in the society news section of the paper. Parker always appeared in the business news section.

She followed Jay out of the coffee bar, positioned the pitchers on a tray and stepped back to examine the arrangement she'd made on top of the credenza.

''Looks like you've been doing this for years. Valerie couldn't have done better.''

Jay had said exactly what Abby thirsted to hear. She exhaled and turned a brilliant smile toward him.

''Jay, I've been looking for you.''

Her smile vanishing instantly, Abby's gaze flew to the doorway where Parker stood.

Something unidentifiable flashed in his eyes and she wondered if she should have announced his brother's arrival.

''And now you've found me,'' Jay said lightly.

''Pestering my assistant, I see.'' Parker walked forward with uncharacteristic slowness and tossed file folders onto the oval conference table.

''Just giving her a hand with the meeting preps.''

Parker glanced at the credenza. ''All appears to be in order.''

Though on the surface, both men were speaking in nonconfrontational tones, Abby sensed an underlying tension between them. Time to leave. ''Do you need anything else, Mr. Laird?''

''Would you bring me the map I left on my worktable?''

Abby hurried into Parker's office, uncertain whether he was angry or not. Surely she didn't have to announce his own brother.

Abby rolled the map and headed back to the conference room. The two men were visible through the doorway. Parker had opened the files and was speaking to Jay, who wore a resigned look as he flipped through the papers in them.

"I would rather hire my own team," he was saying as Abby quietly placed the map at Parker's elbow.

"You arrive next week." Parker's voice was clipped. "You have no on-site support personnel and you have no experience."

"I have experience," Jay snapped. "It's different than yours, so you discount it."

The brothers locked gazes. Without blinking, Parker opened another file folder and pushed it toward Jay. "Ian Douglass is a good man with twenty-three years' experience in remote drilling locations."

"I'll consider him. Thanks for the tip."

"It's not a tip. I hired him this morning."

"Then you can un-hire him this afternoon."

Abby held her breath and as discreetly as possible, tried to evaporate from the room.

"Abby, show everyone in here when they arrive."

"Yes, Mr. Laird."

He regarded her without expression, but Jay winked and Abby quickly turned away before Parker could see her smile.

CHAPTER THREE

AS THE men and women arrived for the meeting, Abby showed them in.

Both Laird brothers greeted them. Jay was a flirt and a backslapper with a contagious laugh and none of the intensity that surrounded his brother.

Jay made her smile.

Parker made her nervous.

He expected perfection and she was determined to give it to him. The pressure of wondering when she was going to make a mistake, as she surely would, was wearing on her.

''Here you go, Mr. Danvers.'' She handed coffee to a man wearing a bolo string tie held by a clip with a diamond cut in the shape of Texas.

''Thank you, sweetheart,'' he boomed. ''How's school?''

''I took my final exam last Thursday.''

''Got your grade yet?''

She shook her head.

''You let me know, now, y'hear?''

Abby smiled. Diamond Don Danvers was a character. He loved playing the quintessential Texas oilman where all the younger women were his ''sweethearts'' and all the younger men his ''boys.'' A wildcatter from way back, he'd earned the right to his showmanship. Everybody knew Diamond Don—he made sure of it. Abby had a soft spot for him because he'd stopped and introduced himself the first time he'd noticed her sitting at her desk by the elevator. It didn't matter to him that she was just a secretary, and it didn't matter to him that Parker and his entourage had hiked down the hall. Diamond Don took the extra minute to learn who she was and ever after asked her about school.

Carrying his coffee, Diamond Don approached Parker and Abby shook her head, thinking that there couldn't be two individuals more different in temperament.

Except maybe Parker and his brother.

She hovered around the credenza waiting to see if she should refresh the coffee before the meeting got under way.

"Shall we get started?" Parker asked, though the way he spoke, no one interpreted it as a question.

Recognizing her signal to leave, Abby started for the door. Since Parker taped the meeting, he didn't need her to take notes, but she would remain in Valerie's office in case he buzzed her for anything.

"Good God Almighty, Parker." Diamond Don's voice cut through the murmurs of people getting settled around the table. "What have you done to your coffee, son?"

Abby froze.

Diamond Don took another swallow and grimaced.

It was then that Abby noticed the full mugs sitting in front of everyone.

"Tastes fine to me," Jay announced, and swallowed, though he blinked rapidly and avoided her eyes.

Abby's palms iced as she looked toward Parker.

Staring into his mug, he twirled the liquid around the edges.

"It's a new bean I'm trying." Parker addressed the

group. ''Indonesian Green Volcano. I'm thinking of investing in the farm where it's grown.''

''Green Volcano.'' Diamond Don shook his head. ''Tastes like volcanic ash, all right.'' He set his cup aside. ''I'd give this one a pass, son.''

Fervent murmurs accompanied Diamond Don's pronouncement.

''Make a note not to order that brand anymore, would you, Abby?'' Parker glanced at her before turning his attention to the agenda. ''And have Barbara or Nancy make us some more coffee.''

Abby nodded and escaped.

Back in her office, she shut the door and leaned against it, her eyes closed while she unwound for a few moments. Inhaling, she noticed that she could smell Valerie's perfume. The scent had permeated the office reminding Abby as nothing else that she was only a temporary Executive Assistant.

Abby didn't want to be reminded that she was only temporary. Someday she *wouldn't* be temporary. Crossing to her desk, she made a note about the coffee, asked Nancy to make more, then made another note to spray Valerie's office with nice refreshing pine scent.

Slipping off her pumps, Abby buried her toes in the carpet pile. During the next hour and a half, her telephone was blessedly silent. Either Nancy or Barbara handled all the calls that came in. Abby sorted through all of one box and was making headway on the second when her intercom buzzed.

''Yes, Mr. Laird?''

''Abby, it looks like we'll be eating lunch here.'' Parker's voice was as composed as ever, though this development just shot his schedule all to pieces.

''I'll order sandwiches,'' she said.

"That'll be fine."

Abby stood and stretched her arms over her head. It had been a long morning and she knew she was in for a lengthy afternoon.

Picking up the telephone, she reached for Valerie's Rolodex. The huge round card file wasn't in its customary spot. No wonder there had been so much room on the desk. Abby looked on the window ledge, then by the computer, behind the monitor, on the file cabinets, *in* the file cabinets and in the desk drawer before giving up.

"Do either of you have Valerie's Rolodex?" Abby asked Barbara and Nancy from the doorway.

Both women looked up from their computers and shook their heads.

"It's gone." Abby looked around their office anyway.

Barbara clicked a button on the tape recorder and took off her headphones. "What do you mean, it's gone?"

"I can't find it. I'm supposed to order sandwiches."

Barbara got up from her desk. "Nancy, you've got that deli number, don't you?"

Nodding, Nancy flipped through her own file. "I'll call in the order, but which assortment?"

The three women stared at each other. Valerie's Rolodex contained personal information about everyone who did, or had done, business with Parker Laird.

"Who's in the meeting?" Barbara asked.

"Well, Diamond Don." Abby tried to remember the rest, but her growing panic wiped their names from her mind.

"So we'll have at least one roast beef," Nancy

murmured. ''I thought I saw a woman in a red suit go by.''

Fighting to control her runaway emotions, Abby nodded.

''That'll be the corporate lawyer handling the El Bahar setup. And I saw Jay...'' Barbara looked off into space. ''It's probably the same bunch who met last Monday.''

Nancy nodded. ''I'll order the same sandwich platter.''

''Make sure Diamond Don's roast beef is rare,'' Barbara reminded her.

''Gotcha.''

Breathing easier, Abby leaned against the file cabinet. ''Thanks.'' Only now would she admit to herself that she'd been afraid Nancy and Barbara wouldn't support her. If they hadn't been so helpful, Abby might have done something stupid like interrupt the meeting to ask Parker what kind of sandwiches to order.

Looking distracted, Barbara walked into Valerie's office. Abby followed her and watched as Barbara looked in all the same places Abby had.

Nancy appeared in the doorway a few moments later. ''Find it?''

''No, and I don't think we're going to,'' Abby said, a queasiness settling in her stomach.

Barbara looked at her. ''You think Valerie took it with her?'' she asked bluntly.

Abby sank onto the desk chair. ''Don't you?''

''Why would she do that?'' Nancy protested. ''It doesn't make any sense. She *knows* we'll need her notes to—oh.''

She and Barbara exchanged a look and Abby knew they were remembering their conversation in the ladies' room—the one about Abby failing. She was remembering it, too.

By taking the old Rolodex, with its years' worth of notes and observations, Valerie had seen to it that Abby couldn't possibly slip seamlessly into her place. All Parker's hotel preferences, special instructions, favorite restaurants and the wait staff in those restaurants, even who took what in his or her coffee and names of spouses and children—all the little details that contributed to an extra edge in Parker's business dealings were in that Rolodex.

"I don't suppose any of the information was computerized?" Abby asked.

Both women shook their heads.

Think, Abby commanded herself, though she wanted to shriek—preferably at Valerie. "Then we'll have to recreate Valerie's notes."

Nancy rolled her eyes. "You've got to be kidding."

Staring at her toes as they dug into the carpet, Abby swiveled her chair from side to side. "The thing of it is," she began with elaborate casualness, "not having the information in Valerie's files makes us *all* look bad—including Valerie."

"How do you figure that?" There was a belligerent defensiveness in Nancy's voice.

Barbara was silent and Abby guessed that she was figuring things out for herself.

"I've only been working in this department since March and you've been here how long?"

"Three years." Nancy tilted her chin up. "So what?"

"I know you've worked here longer." Abby looked at Barbara, who crossed her arms. "Naturally, Mr. Laird expects you both to know more about the routine than I do, because if you haven't learned *anything* after working here all those years...'' She allowed her voice to trail off as Barbara and Nancy exchanged looks.

''We'd look either stupid or lazy.'' Nancy propped her hand on her hip and shook her head in disgust. ''So how does that make Valerie look bad?''

''Because she hired us,'' Barbara answered.

''And because she's the manager,'' Abby added. ''In the management course I'm taking, we learned about delegating and about making provisions for when you're out of the office. That way, everything functions smoothly. Did you know that there isn't a Policy and Procedure manual?''

''There doesn't have to be,'' Nancy said. ''The policy is to do what we're told. The procedure to do it as fast as possible.''

Barbara laughed, but Abby didn't. ''What if Valerie *doesn't* have the Rolodex, or what if she decides she likes Greece so much that she doesn't want to come back?'' Abby didn't wait for a response. Besides, everyone knew Valerie would be back. ''I'm turning my notes into a manual so one of you can take over in case *I'm* not here.''

By the time she finished speaking, both women were nodding in agreement.

''I've made my own notes,'' Nancy offered, with the first genuine smile she'd directed toward Abby since Valerie had announced that Abby would be her replacement. ''I'm the one who usually makes the phone calls.''

''Great.'' Abby beamed at her.

''I know a thing or two,'' Barbara added. ''I'll start a file.'' She headed toward her office, then stopped and glanced back at Abby. "I really hate looking incompetent."

"Of course, we'll be making Valerie look good, too," Nancy grumbled. "And it was mean of her to take the Rolodex."

"Maybe she didn't do it on purpose," Abby said.

Both women gave her a look.

"And maybe she did." Abby grinned and they all shared a laugh.

Before following Nancy back through the connecting door, Barbara pointed to one of the black boxes. "Is this box sorted?"

"Yes." Abby hadn't wanted to mention the pile of work. If she hadn't had to stop and prepare for the meeting, she would have distributed it before now. "Could you use someone from the typing pool downstairs? With Valerie gone, we've effectively had our work force cut by twenty-five percent. I don't want to get behind."

"Good idea." Barbara scooped up the pile of papers. "If we nab some leftover sandwiches, Nancy and I can stay through lunch and have typing work ready by one-thirty."

Abby nodded, grimacing as a thought occurred to her. "What kind of sandwich does Mr. Laird like? I didn't even think to ask."

"Weird sandwiches," Barbara answered. "He likes to be surprised and the deli experiments on him."

Parker Laird liked to be surprised? The same Parker Laird who fanatically scheduled his days in fifteen-minute blocks?

"Tell her about the mushrooms," Nancy called from the other office.

"Oh, yeah. Last time, they sent grilled portabella

mushrooms and tomato on sourdough.'' Barbara sighed. ''Heavenly.''

''A mushroom sandwich? I'll take chicken salad, thank you very much,'' Abby said.

As soon as Barbara disappeared into her office, Abby closed her eyes and exhaled. She'd handled this hurdle and convinced Barbara and Nancy to support her. She'd acted *managerial.* Her business professor would have been proud.

But it was Parker she wanted to please.

Thanks to Jay, he was already forty-five minutes behind schedule. His brother was going to have to learn how to facilitate meetings if he had any intention of returning from El Bahar within a year.

Lunch remains were scattered across the conference table and people had lingered, gabbing aimlessly for at least twenty minutes after all business had been conducted. Parker had allowed ten minutes for socializing prior to the meeting. He failed to understand why it was necessary to supplement the allotted time during business hours. It was inefficient.

Jay was inefficient and nothing Parker did seemed to change his ways.

Parker eyed the frown on his brother's face and felt the minutes tick away.

''Surely it isn't necessary that *I* attend the—'' Jay broke off and scooted the gold and black invitation toward him. ''Chamber Music Preservation Board Awards luncheon.'' He grimaced. ''How many of these things are you on, anyway?''

''*We* are on dozens. Thank Mother.''

''Then let *her* go.''

''She is.''

''Then *you* go.''

"I'll be at a Zoological Society fund-raiser."

"Trade you." Jay grinned.

"Ordinarily that wouldn't be a problem, but continuity is a factor here."

"English, please."

Parker leveled a look at him. "You're leaving next week, so be a good boy and accept the pretty plaque."

"And what did I do?"

"You donated fifty thousand dollars to refurbish the Green Room at Allen Hall."

Jay gave a low whistle. "I'm very generous."

Parker spared a brief smile. "The Symphony Guild is wining and dining you tomorrow night."

"Why?" Jay looked pained.

"Because you're leaving next week and they hope you won't forget them."

"Why? Is their Green Room shabby, too?"

"Not anymore."

Jay heaved an exaggerated sigh. "Parker, how did I get a reputation as a classical music lover?"

"By donating generously to the arts in Houston. Mother is very pleased."

Jay narrowed his eyes. "*You* sicced those stuffy music people on me, didn't you?"

Parker met his gaze. "I ran out of wall space for plaques."

Jay drummed his fingers on the conference table. "Tell me, am I free any night this week?"

Parker noted that Jay had not brought his agenda with him—the cordovan leather agenda Parker had given him. Typical. He consulted his own planning book, where he was keeping track of Jay's schedule. "Let's see. Thursday is the Aria Society." He looked up. "Another farewell dinner."

"It could be worse. It could be the whole opera group."

"That's on Friday night. A performance in your honor."

"Oh, joy." Jay groaned and dropped his head to the table.

"Now tonight… You'll enjoy tonight. The University of Houston Jazz Ensemble. Dinner and dancing." Parker was planning to go to that one himself. Dancing meant contact with women. Parker knew better than to allow Jay unchaperoned contact with women so near to his departure for El Bahar.

Jay fell in love quickly, deeply, and frequently. When in the early impassioned rush of a new romance, he was prone to making extravagant—and usually expensive—gestures.

Therefore, Parker was determined that there would be no new romance before his brother left for El Bahar, which was why he'd gotten quite a jolt at seeing Jay flirting with Abby earlier. As his father would say, if it wore a skirt, Jay noticed it.

He'd have to remind Ian Douglass to leave his kilt in Scotland, Parker thought.

"I hope I'm up for the symphony deal," Jay informed him. "Since I have to vacate the condo by the fifteenth, I'll be moving in with Mother tomorrow."

Parker sent a fervent prayer of thanks to the real estate gods and surreptitiously scrawled a reminder that the Realtor had earned the extra commission he'd promised her. With Jay living with their mother, his dating style would be hampered considerably.

"I will assume this means you'll have a household shipment ready this week?" It would still arrive in El Bahar weeks after Jay, something he'd pointed out to his brother before.

"I suppose so," Jay confirmed.

Almost home free, Parker thought as he punched the intercom on the telephone. "Abby, there are some extra sandwiches in here if you and the others haven't eaten yet."

"Thanks, Mr. Laird."

"Abby?" Jay raised his eyebrows.

"My assistant while Valerie's gone." Parker watched for his reaction. "You met her this morning?"

"Oh, the wholesome one." Jay smiled impersonally. "Seems nice. Awfully young."

"I wasn't so much older when I began running this company." Parker found himself defending her.

Jay stood. "Parker, you were never young."

Abby came through the door, darting a nervous look toward Parker, which unaccountably annoyed him, and smiling slightly at his brother, which annoyed him further.

Jay grinned at her and Abby's smile broadened.

What was it about Jay that women found irresistible? Parker wondered. Were they that easily swayed by his charmingly facile smile?

For years, Parker had watched his younger brother wheedle his way out of chores, punishments and responsibility. He'd watched his mother's eyes light when Jay entered the room and knew that, though she loved them both, she adored Jay.

He had a way with people, Parker acknowledged, but he still hadn't accomplished one solid thing in his twenty-six years. Parker hoped the El Bahar project would be the making of him. After a year or so in the Arabian desert, Jay would return seasoned and ready to take more responsibility in the running of Laird Drilling and Exploration.

At least that was the plan—a plan Parker was determined to put into place.

"Great job on the meeting, Abby," Jay said. "And those sandwiches—" he kissed his fingers "—heavenly."

Parker frowned.

She laughed. "I didn't make them. I ordered them from the deli down the street."

"And you dialed very well."

She laughed again.

What was funny about that? The whole conversation sounded pointlessly absurd to Parker. "Abby, when you finish lunch, would you meet me in my office?" He checked his watch. "Say, in twenty minutes?"

"A whole twenty minutes for lunch?" Jay raised his eyebrows. "Careful, Parker. You'll get a reputation as a softie."

"Twenty minutes is plenty of time," Abby broke in.

"No, it's not," Jay insisted. "You're entitled to take an hour like everyone else."

"Not all of us," Parker said, and snapped his agenda shut, "have an hour to take."

With a curt nod toward his brother, he left the conference room, walking quickly to his desk. Jay might want to fritter away the afternoon, but he had work to do.

Precisely twenty minutes later, Abby knocked once on the open door, then entered his office.

By the skin of her teeth, she'd finished going through the black boxes and had sorted the papers into three color-coded files. Red was for urgent, blue was for Parker's signature and the yellow file contained reports and information-only items.

And, on her own, Abby had added a fourth file in pink. Pink was an I-don't-know file. She'd chosen pink, thinking of it as a pale red. Now, she wished she'd chosen green or orange. The neon pink folder looked too bright and out of place in Parker's office.

She slipped into the chaïr, opened the master calendar and clicked on the tape recorder.

Sure enough, Parker reached for the pink folder first.

"Those are nonurgent items," she explained before he could ask.

"Nonurgent?"

"They require action, but not immediately."

Nodding, he looked through the folder. The pink was so bright, it tinged the underside of his jaw and neck. She should have chosen the green.

He changed two papers to the red file, one to the yellow, then closed the folder and moved it to the right side of his desk. "Good idea."

Abby relaxed marginally.

Parker glanced through the yellow and blue files next and Abby was pleased that he didn't move any. She'd apparently sorted correctly.

Next, he opened the red file and Abby prepared for a flurry of instructions. By the time Parker had reached the end of the file, Abby had a long list of assignments and schedule changes. How on earth would she get everything done today?

The recorder clicked off when the tape ran out after forty-five minutes. Abby was ready for a break.

But she'd known this position would be intense. This is what she'd wanted, so she'd better get used to it.

''Thanks, Abby,'' Parker said as she gathered the papers. ''Do you have any questions?''

Abby shook her head and stood.

Parker stood as well. ''You're not a coffee drinker, are you?''

''No, sir.'' Abby heard the ''sir'' leave her mouth and gritted her teeth.

Parker let it pass. ''I didn't think so. Come with me.''

What now? Abby followed Parker into the conference room. He went into the little coffee bar and gestured for her to join him.

Abby set her files and the scheduling book on the conference table before standing next to the sink.

Parker emptied the morning's coffee grounds into the trash.

''Oh! I'm sorry, I should have done that.'' Thinking she was being reprimanded, Abby's face warmed.

''No, you shouldn't. The cleaning staff will take care of it,'' he said calmly, and proceeded to wash the coffeepot and filter while Abby stood awkwardly beside him.

As earlier with Jay, she was aware of the cramped space and was standing closer to her boss than she was comfortable doing. She was close enough to see the faint grayness of his beard beneath his skin. Close enough to see the blond tips of his dark eyelashes and faint lines at the corner of his eye. Close enough to see the razor-precise edge of his haircut.

Close enough to be more aware of him as a man than as her boss.

Sure she harbored secret fantasies about Parker Laird. Every woman who worked here did. He was the perfect secret fantasy type—attractive, available, rich and powerful.

And there wasn't a chance in the world that he'd ever think of her as anything other than his temporary assistant.

Abby held herself stiffly in order to avoid any accidental contact as he moved, and tried to forget that she was standing only inches away from the man running an international company.

And he was washing the coffee things!

Abby grabbed a tea towel and wiped the outside of the pot after he thoroughly rinsed the soap from it.

"Thanks." He reached into the overhead cabinets and studied the brown bags of coffee. "I enjoy coffee. A lot. And like most coffee aficionados, I'm very particular about the way I take my coffee. I imagine you have the same feelings about your...tea?"

Abby nodded.

He selected a bag. "So you understand."

She nodded again.

"But I've cut back on coffee, so I want to make every cup I drink count."

"That makes sense."

"We've already scheduled three meetings here this week, so I foresee gallons of coffee making in your future."

"So you want me to learn to make it the way you like it."

"Exactly." Parker pulled open the sealed bag of beans and withdrew a square measure from the drawer. "Fill one of these for each twelve-cup pot of coffee." He pointed out a smaller one. "Measure one of those for each two cups of water."

Abby stepped closer, watching carefully as he measured the beans into the grinder. Along with the coffee aroma, she smelled something else—a cottony scent that she finally identified as laundry starch.

Parker always wore crisp white shirts with French cuffs and a dark suit. During the day, he took off the jacket and very occasionally, Abby had seen him with his sleeves rolled up, but the next time she saw him with the cuffs fastened, the sleeves bore no signs of wrinkles on the arms. She'd suspected that he'd ducked into the his private suite to change shirts.

She leaned closer and inhaled carefully. Yes, laundry starch. So this is what power smells like, she thought. Coffee and laundry starch.

"Grind the beans for five seconds," Parker instructed.

Abby pushed on the grinder and counted to herself.

"Let's check." Parker took off the top. "We don't want too fine a grind or the coffee will have bitterness to it. This could use another two seconds."

When Abby finished, he let her study the texture of the grounds before emptying them into the basket.

Abby knew she hadn't been this precise when preparing coffee for the meeting this morning. Naturally, Valerie hadn't told her that Mr. Laird was so particular about his coffee. Frankly, all coffee tasted bad to Abby, but he was the boss.

She studied him as he used a brush to remove the last of the grounds from the grinder, liking the way he focused completely on the task at hand, minor though it was.

Abby was beginning to learn that once something had Parker Laird's attention, it had *all* his attention.

"Next, fill the reservoir with cold water." He opened the tiny refrigerator and withdrew a bottle of water.

Abby had used warm water directly from the tap. Why did it have to be cold? Weren't they going to heat it up? Wouldn't hot water be faster?

"If you use hot water, it will taste like the plumbing." Parker answered her unspoken question.

"Oh." At least she hadn't used hot water this morning, but she'd thought about it, since she'd been in a hurry. Maybe using cold water would improve the taste of her tea.

Parker positioned the pot and turned on the machine. "And that's all there is to it."

"Thanks. I'll be more careful next time." Abby resealed the coffee bag.

"Try a cup of this." He gestured to the coffee dripping into the pot. "You might find you like coffee after all."

"Maybe." Abby wrinkled her nose and stepped aside so Parker could leave. "I'll clean up here."

Parker's arm brushed against hers as he moved past.

Abby swallowed as every nerve in the area retained the memory of his touch. Good grief.

She put away the coffee, wiped the counter, then tossed the paper towel into the trash.

And then she saw it—the empty bag of coffee that she'd used this morning.

Abby bent and picked it out of the trash can, then she opened the cabinet door. This bag was like all the other bags of coffee.

"Abby?" Parker appeared in the doorway. "I've changed my mind. Would you call Peter Frostwood and tell him that if he gets up here right now, I'll see him?"

Abby looked up from the bag she held. "There's no such coffee as Indonesian Green Volcano, is there?"

It was a moment before Parker answered. "No." He stared at her.

It tastes like volcanic ash. Diamond Don's comment took on a horrible new meaning. *Her coffee had tasted so bad, no one had drunk it.* And Parker had told them it was a new kind of bean.

How awful. But as Abby stared back at Parker, her mouth quivered as she fought first the smile, then the laughter that burbled out anyway.

And then they were both laughing. *He has a sense of humor*, she thought with wonder and relief. "Thanks, Parker."

"No problem." He grinned back at her, looking a lot like Jay.

It was only after she was back in her office that she realized how easily she'd called him by name.

CHAPTER FOUR

PARKER missed Valerie.

Not that Abby had done a bad job, but he hadn't realized how much he'd sought and relied on his Executive Assistant's opinions—probably a habit from his teenage years. Valerie had been there. His father usually wasn't.

Swiveling to face the windows in his office, Parker stared at the Houston freeway below him, watching the waves of traffic as he frequently did.

Only Valerie and a couple of board members remained from the time his father had run Laird Drilling. It was Valerie who'd helped smooth the transition from father to son and Valerie, rather than his mother, with whom he discussed the problem of Jay.

Valerie usually alerted Parker when Jay was in trouble. Jay confided in her, obviously thinking that hearing bad news from Valerie was better than hearing it from him. Parker had lost count of the number of times he'd rescued his brother from situations he couldn't afford or promises he couldn't keep.

Technically, Jay owned the same percentage of Laird Drilling that Parker did, but had yet to show more than a peripheral interest in the company, and then only when he was between girlfriends—as he was now.

Jay's problem was that he had too much money and had been spoiled by their mother.

Why should he work? Everything had been given

to him and he expected a high position with a fancy title just for being born a Laird.

Parker stared out onto the horizon. This was an old argument and one he didn't want to dwell on now. He'd offered Jay real jobs that would allow him to learn about the business, but Jay felt they were beneath him and would quit after a few weeks.

Valerie had given Parker the idea of finding a project for which Jay could be totally responsible, succeeding or failing on his own, without big brother available to rescue him. For once, he'd have to live with the consequences of his actions and Parker was all for that. He knew constantly rescuing Jay wasn't right, but too often Jay's troubles affected Parker or the company as much as Jay, so Parker had no choice.

Heading up the El Bahar drilling field was perfect. It was important enough to satisfy Jay and remote enough to satisfy Parker. Quitting would be more difficult in the middle of the desert.

Meeting women would be more difficult in the desert.

Since breaking up with Lisa, a relationship that had appeared more serious than usual, Jay had been uncharacteristically subdued, though with Valerie gone, Parker couldn't be certain exactly what Jay was up to—or who he was up to it with. He'd counted on their mother to keep him out of trouble this week even though she had a blind spot where her younger son was concerned. The fact that Jay was scheduled to spend the next year in an isolated desert country on the other side of the world hadn't set well with her.

Parker wasn't certain he could depend on his mother to restrain Jay and he was tired of planning for at least one of them to go to all these dinners and other time-wasters with Jay.

The fact was, tonight's jazz concert was the first gathering Parker had looked forward to in a long time. People complained that he didn't socialize enough. Well, tonight, they'd get both the Laird brothers. Unattached. Without dates. Wealthy bachelors, free for the plucking.

The local tabloids would go wild.

There was a knock on his door and Abby's curly head appeared. "Parker?"

"Yes, Abby?" He automatically checked his watch as she hurried across the room.

His office was too big, he thought while he waited for her. It took too long for people to get to his desk. He'd move the desk toward the door, except then he'd lose the window view.

"Peter Frostwood just called from Louisiana."

Parker groaned. Peter had flown out there this morning. "That well didn't blow, did it?"

Abby nodded. "He'll be calling back in five minutes. I pulled the project files and a map of the area for you." She set the files on his desk.

"Great. Put him through when he calls."

She hesitated. "Mr. Frostwood mentioned that the well is near a nature preserve. I have Nancy looking up the media in that area in case you'd like to prepare a press release."

Parker had already turned his attention to the well production specifications. He blinked up at her. "Good thinking. Yes, I would."

She smiled and a becoming peach color tinted her cheeks.

It occurred to Parker that she had every right to be pleased with herself. She'd shown initiative and an accurate grasp of the situation. It also occurred to him that she was a junior employee who'd taken on a senior position and had done an admirable job. He ought to tell her so.

''Abby?''

''Yes?'' She'd already turned to leave.

''I...'' Expressing praise was difficult for Parker. ''You've done a superlative job filling in for Valerie, though I might not always express my gratitude adequately.'' *I sound like my father.* ''But I do appreciate the work you've done.'' Talk about awkward. He probably shouldn't have bothered.

But Abby, after a startled widening of her eyes, rewarded him with a blinding smile that momentarily wiped everything else from his mind. ''Thanks! Barbara, Nancy and I have tried to make certain you didn't miss Valerie *too* much. I'll be sure and tell them you're pleased.''

A beat went by as Parker blinked against the brilliance of her smile. ''Certainly.''

Flashing another smile, Abby hurried from the office.

Parker stared after her. She'd...*blossomed* under his praise, stiff and stilted though it had been. He should hand out kudos to his employees more often. He knew this already, but a reminder never hurt.

After all, hadn't he lived for a complimentary word from his father? Approval from his father had been so rare that Parker had cherished the words. A few more wouldn't have made him value them any less.

Abby had also been quick to include the staff rather than taking sole credit. A sign of confidence and intelligence. He'd remember that.

His thoughts were interrupted by the incoming call from Peter Frostwood.

''Hey, Peter. How bad is it?''

''The fire's about under control, but oil's leaked out

and the mess looks worse than it is.'' A beating sound grew in the background. ''News helicopters are hovering,'' Peter shouted into the telephone. ''What now?''

''I can hear them.'' Abby had called that one right. ''We're preparing a statement.''

''It had better be a whopper. Can you make a face-to-face?''

Parker winced. ''If I come there, they'll think the situation is worse than it is. If I don't, Laird Drilling will be accused of trying to downplay an environmental disaster. Let me get back to you.''

After hanging up the telephone, Parker turned to the window. He should call a board member, or the executive vice president in charge of public relations, and would eventually, but he'd rather talk to Valerie first. Valerie knew about the ''Jay factor.'' If she were here, he'd send her to the jazz dinner with his brother tonight and head for Louisiana. Unfortunately, Valerie wasn't here.

But Abby was.

Before he thought twice about it, Parker was reaching for the intercom button, then decided to go to her office himself.

He found her on the floor surrounded by papers from the black boxes.

''Don't get up,'' he said when she hastily set aside a pile from her lap. ''I wanted your thoughts on the well fire.''

She looked bemused. ''Should I point out here that I know nothing about well fires?''

''That doesn't matter.'' He reached into the box and grabbed the top three inches of papers, then sat beside her on the floor and absently started sorting them. "As an average citizen, what do you think when the press reports an oil spill or a well fire?"

"That the next time I go to the beach, I'm going to have to watch for great globs of icky tar."

"Environmental impact, then." He reached across her to toss papers at the yellow file. They scattered to one side.

"Nancy has to enter this report into the spreadsheet," Abby murmured and stacked the papers.

"How would you want the company to respond?"

Abby looked at him as though he'd lost his mind. "I'd want to know that they plan to clean up their own mess, quickly and without whining or excuses."

"That's what I thought." Parker ripped open a letter, scanned the contents and searched for a pen. Abby gave him hers and he scrawled "okay" on the letter and handed it to her. "Would hearing that message from the CEO of the company reassure you, or would you think the problem must be serious if he's involved?"

She gazed at him. "Is this a test?"

"No, I'm asking your opinion." He opened another letter. "I found that Valerie has a different take on things. Sometimes I feel the board is too insular and I like to have a balance of opinions."

She looked so nonplussed he felt compelled to add, "That doesn't mean I pay any attention to what anyone says."

Abby laughed. "That's more like it."

Parker leaned against the file cabinet. "So. What do you think?"

Abby sat back on her heels and pushed a stray curl off her cheek. "You know, I never really thought about it, but if a spokesman says something, the message doesn't have the same impact as if the president or somebody says it.'' She looked at him. ''But surely you've faced this situation before?''

''Yes, though I'm proud to say not often.'' Parker wrote ''schedule meeting'' on the letter he'd opened and put it in Abby's red file. ''The truth is, I don't like dealing with the press. No matter what I say, they'll twist it to sound the way they want. That's why I generally avoid them.''

''You probably shouldn't this time. Remember the nature preserve.''

Abby sounded remarkably like Valerie. They both had an innate common sense. Maybe, just maybe, Abby could handle Jay tonight. Or handle Jay as much as anyone could. But suppose he did send her with Jay. Though his brother had several immature character traits, rudeness wasn't one of them. No, even though Abby's type didn't appeal to him, Jay wouldn't leave her to fend for herself while he took up with another woman. Yes, Abby might be the answer.

''You're right. I should go.'' He got to his feet.

''Whatever you do, don't make one of those canned speeches that sound like you've had twelve lawyers pick it apart for liability.''

''That's their job.''

''But...'' She sighed. ''I'd rather see you hop on the company plane and arrive all breathless and admit you don't have a canned statement. *Then* you stress the new safety procedures you've initiated and that you wanted to see them in action for yourself because, fortunately, you don't often get the opportunity and though this wasn't much of a test, look how well the people and equipment responded...'' She waved her hand. ''And so on. Tell the reporters when everything will be cleaned up and invite them back then.''

"Offer the press the story I want them to have, right?"

"Right."

He grinned down at her. "Maybe I should transfer you to Public Relations. You're a natural."

"I'd rather you didn't," Abby responded seriously. "This job is the one I've always wanted."

The real job or the one you've imagined it to be? Parker stared into her clear, blue, inexperienced eyes. Abby hadn't had to face a crisis yet. She hadn't had to deal with *Jay* yet. She might as well start now. "You are aware of what a trip to Louisiana will do to my schedule, which brings up something else. I'm supposed to attend the jazz concert and dinner tonight with Jay." Parker chose his next words carefully. "If Valerie were here, I'd send her in my place." He could see Abby's eyes light up. "Valerie's position would be to…keep Jay focused on his impending departure to El Bahar… What is so funny?"

The smile she'd been visibly fighting gave way to laughter. "Everybody knows Valerie would only be there to keep Jay out of trouble. Oops!" Abby slapped her hand over her mouth.

His mouth twisted. "Everybody knows?"

She nodded.

Great. Parker wasn't surprised, though. "Then you know you have a challenge ahead of you."

"You mean you want *me* to go to the jazz concert tonight?"

"Yes, I mean I want you to go to the jazz concert tonight."

"To chaperone your brother."

"That's about the size of it." Though Parker briefly wondered who'd chaperone Abby. She was a starry-eyed innocent from a small town. But, Parker reminded himself, Jay wasn't interested in her. He'd even forgotten who she was. No, Abby would be fine. Just fine.

"Okay," she said, flashing some leg as she got to her feet and reached for the scheduling book.

"Okay," Parker repeated, having second thoughts at the sight of her leg. She might be a small-town girl, but she had big-city legs.

Later, after they'd ripped apart his schedule and made arrangements for his flight to Louisiana, Parker handed Abby a royal blue and silver invitation to tonight's dinner dance and concert. "The theme is the blues, as in they're singing the blues. 'Blue Jay,' that sort of thing."

"Clever," she commented in a thoughtful voice. "Everyone is supposed to dress in blue, I see."

Parker felt like an idiot. "Do you have something blue to wear?"

She smiled wryly. "Jeans?"

Her eyes are blue. The thought came from nowhere. "Call the personal shopper at Neiman-Marcus and have them bring over some appropriate dresses. They'll charge it to the Laird account."

Abby's chin tilted up and she stood straighter. "I can buy my own clothes."

"It's much faster this way. Trust me." He began clearing the surface of his desk.

"No, I mean I can pay for my own clothes."

Parker looked up, belatedly realizing he'd hurt her pride. "This is different." He gestured to the invitation she held. "It's not right for you to have to buy something special for tonight."

"Do you buy Valerie clothes?"

She was stubborn. That was a good thing. She'd need to be stubborn when dealing with Jay, but Parker didn't have time for stubborn now. "I don't know what arrangements Valerie had with my father when she first became his Executive Assistant, but I do know what I pay her and what I'm paying you. Think of this as a uniform for the job."

While Abby eyed him uncertainly as she considered his words, Parker called the Laird pilot. "I'm heading out now, Chris." When he hung up the telephone, he could tell by her face that Abby had come to a decision.

"All right, I'll accept your offer, but only because I really and truly have nothing blue except my navy blue suit."

Parker closed his briefcase. "You should." He came out from behind his desk, pausing as he drew even with her. "Blue would go great with your eyes."

Though it was true, he hadn't meant to say that out loud. She looked as startled as he felt. "Have a good time tonight," he added gruffly, and hurried out the door, all the time picturing Abby in blue.

Abby had no idea evening dresses came in so many shades of blue.

Parker's office had been turned into a changing room.

"I'm so sorry we don't have a better selection, but many of our clients will be attending this evening," Jolie, the personal shopper, apologized as she unzipped plastic bags. Half a dozen dresses hung from a silver rack.

Casually, Abby ran her hand down one heavily beaded sleeve until she got to the price tag, at which point she got such a bad case of sticker shock that she resolved not to look at the prices anymore.

When she'd told Nancy and Barbara what was going on, they'd thought she was nuts for objecting at all, so Abby supposed she shouldn't.

She just didn't feel right about having her employer buy her clothes, but after seeing that one price, knew she couldn't have afforded to buy any of these dresses herself. She'd be representing Parker Laird and Laird Drilling tonight, she told herself. She needed to look the part.

"No, not that one." Jolie returned the beaded one to the bag. "It looks far too old for you." She held up a stretchy teal number with fringe.

"Absolutely not." Abby would look like a country-western singer in that getup.

Next, Jolie held up a long slim column in royal blue. "This would look *fabulous* on you."

Abby reached for it. Subdued. That was more like it. A nice high jewel collar. Discreet. She flipped the hanger.

Backless.

Thin spaghetti straps crisscrossed down to the waist. "I don't think so." Abby returned the garment to Jolie.

"You sure?" Jolie smiled slyly. "There'll be a lot of high rollers there tonight, if you know what I mean."

"I know what you mean," Abby said. "But this is business."

"That doesn't mean a girl can't make the most of a situation."

"How about this one?" Hurriedly, Abby reached for a swirl of chiffon in midnight-blue. A full skirt was topped by a fitted bodice, transparent sleeves and satin collar and cuffs with rhinestone buttons.

Jolie grimaced. "It's a mother-of-the-bride-type

dress. You're going to a jazz concert. Why not look a little jazzier?''

''I'm not a jazzy person.'' Abby took the dress into Parker's private quarters. Even though she knew he wouldn't mind, she felt as though she was trespassing on consecrated ground.

In the few minutes Abby took to slip into the chiffon dress, she glanced around the room, disappointed that there was nothing personal in it. Not counting the weights and treadmill by the window, there were no photographs, no bowling trophies or anything that hinted at what kind of man Parker was.

She might as well be in a hotel room, but wasn't that exactly how Parker considered his office suite?

As she buttoned the rhinestone buttons, Abby studied herself in the full-length mirror behind the door.

She looked dressy, but discreet. Proper. This dress would take her anywhere and it was in a timeless, if staid, style. Perfect for the first piece in her official Executive Assistant wardrobe.

Satisfied, Abby went out to show Jolie.

''Well, there's certainly nothing wrong with the fit,'' Jolie commented, pinching the material at the waist. ''If you had more time, I might suggest nipping in a little at the waist, but since the dress is belted, you can get away with wearing it as is.''

''Then I'll take it.''

''Wouldn't you like to see the other dresses?''

Abby shook her head. ''This one is exactly right. I understand you brought shoes?''

Wearing a disappointed frown, Jolie unzipped a hanging bag with quilted compartments. ''You can't go wrong with a sedate black pump in *peau de soie*.'' She pulled out a pair.

Abby stepped into them. They were her size, but

they pinched. She walked across the floor and knew her feet would never last the night. "Do you have any other shoes?"

"Sure." Jolie pulled apart the bag, revealing another half a dozen pairs. "Here's gold, but not with that dress. I think I brought a pair in silver."

Abby kicked off the shoes, sinking her abused feet into the carpet. As she returned the shoes to Jolie, a pair of pale blue sandals dusted with diamonds twinkled at her. "Oh." She pulled one out.

"Aren't those gorgeous?" Jolie handed Abby another pair of shoes that looked orthopedic by comparison. "They were made for the dress in this bag." Jolie tapped the opaque bag next to Abby.

"They were made to go with it?" Abby had never heard of such a thing.

"Sure."

Abby stared at a chunky black pump in one hand and the ethereal sandal in the other.

Be practical, advised her conscience.

What would it hurt to look at the other dress? whispered another voice.

"Here." Jolie unzipped the bag. "It won't hurt to just look at the other dress."

Abby told herself not to look.

But, of course, she did.

As soon as Jolie withdrew the shimmering fabric, Abby knew she was lost.

The dress was one of those lethally elegant creations no woman could resist, but not every woman could wear. It was only a sleeveless, fitted sheath, but the richness of the pale blue fabric and the sparkle of thousands of the tiniest diamonds made it memorable.

"Want try it on?" Jolie held it out to her.

Don't you dare! "Oh, I don't think..."

Try doesn't have to mean buy.

"Don't think. Go on." Jolie pushed her toward Parker's suite. "Take the shoes."

As if in a dream, Abby took the shoes and the dress and floated toward Parker's suite. She undid the rhinestone buttons and stepped out of the navy-blue mother-of-the-bride dress.

"I'll never get this dress over my hips," she muttered as she stepped into the twinkling blue sheath.

But she did.

"It'll be too short." She zipped it all the way up before looking at herself in the mirror.

The hemline brushed the tops of her knees.

The armholes weren't too high or too deep.

The neckline was perfectly proper—both front and back.

"Well, if the shoes fit, it'll be a miracle." Abby unfastened the jeweled buckles, braced herself on the doorjamb and slipped the shoes onto her feet. "Okay, so they fit, but I can't walk in heels this high."

Did her toes peep out too much? Staring at her feet, Abby took a step, then another. The shoes were lighter than air and she didn't have a bit of trouble. Of course, the carpeting must help.

Stopping in front of the mirror, she took a breath, then raised her eyes to meet her reflection.

"Oh!"

There was a knock at the door. "How does the dress look? May I come in?" Jolie pushed open the door and stared at Abby. "I feel like a fairy godmother." Jolie grabbed for the discarded chiffon. "Selling you anything else would harm my professional reputation."

"Well, I wouldn't want you to lose your job..." Abby could hardly believe that she was the elegant woman reflected in the mirror. The elegant *attractive* woman.

''What are you going to do with your hair?'' Jolie asked.

''I—I hadn't thought about it.''

Stepping behind her, Jolie unfastened the clip and Abby's curly hair exploded.

''Wow. Is that natural?''

Sighing, Abby nodded and tried to gather her hair in the clip.

''Hey, leave it. There are women who pay a fortune to get their hair to do that.'' Jolie stepped into the bathroom and opened the water taps. ''Let's get some steam going and loosen up those curls.'' She unzipped Abby, tossed the dress over a chair and pulled her into the bathroom. ''Stay here while I pack up everything.''

Abby was too shocked at finding herself standing in Parker Laird's private quarters in her underwear to argue. She could almost feel her hair curl, she *did* feel her makeup melting and…since when did the furniture have eyes?

''Time's up,'' sang out Jolie several interminable minutes later. ''Your pumpkin is here.''

''What?''

''The limo driver. Says he's here to pick you up.''

The limo!

So far, Abby had experienced a lot of work and none of the glamour of her new position. Parker had seldom left the office for more than lunch. He'd attended no meeting where he'd called for her to hop in the limousine and bring him a needed file. No dash to the airport with her coming along to receive last-minute instructions.

Abby had really wanted to ride in that limousine.

And now she was going to.

She was living her dream and was afraid she was going to wake up, especially if Jolie kept pulling her hair that way.

"Hold still." Jolie brushed locks of Abby's hair around her finger. For some inexplicable reason, her hair behaved for Jolie.

"You don't need to do that."

"Oh, I know, but it's fun. Aren't you having fun?"

"Yes." Abby smiled. "Yes, I'm having a *lot* of fun."

Abby quickly discovered that her fun was just beginning.

After transferring her keys and wedging her bulky wallet into a tiny silver evening purse, Abby was ready to go.

Jolie wrote out the sales receipt, which Abby signed without actually looking at the total, trusting that Jolie was honest and wanted to keep the Laird account.

Any awkwardness she felt at leaving her work clothes in her office vanished the moment Abby stepped into the spacious interior of the luxury car. She was aware of at least one person watching her, probably wondering who she was.

Trying to pretend that being driven was an everyday occurrence, Abby settled against the leather seat.

"Mr. Laird asked that I collect you before Mr. Jay," the driver informed her.

Abby had forgotten all about Jay. "Mr. Laird made his flight okay?"

The driver's eyes met hers in the rearview mirror. "They weren't going to take off without him now, were they?"

Oh. Of course. The company plane. Abby was going to have to start thinking in a whole different way. A rich way.

CHAPTER FIVE

"WELL, hellooo." Jay flashed Abby a white-toothed smile as he sat in the seat across from her.

Abby tugged on the hem of her dress and smiled shyly back.

He raised his eyebrows. "What? No Parker?"

"Mr. Laird had to go to Louisiana and deal with a well fire. He sent me in his place."

"Did he now?" Jay sat back and rubbed his upper lip. "And who are you, sexy angel?"

Taken aback, Abby responded with a surprised laugh. Jay's expression didn't change.

"It's Abby." But no flash of recognition lit his eyes. He truly didn't know who she was. Abby didn't know whether to be thrilled or annoyed. "Parker's assistant while Valerie is away?" she prompted.

"*You're* the little...well, well." His gaze swept over her and before she could guess his intention, he stepped over to her side of the car and sat next to her in a smooth movement that ended with his arm flung carelessly across the back of the seat.

"Do you like jazz?" he asked, flicking a hidden lever that closed the window between the driver and the passenger.

Abby eyed the closing window. "I haven't listened to that type of music enough, except in old movies."

"My father collected jazz recordings. Not all of them are available on compact disc. If you like what you hear tonight, I'll play the rare records for you sometime." During his social patter, Jay opened a side compartment and, with one hand, popped the top off a bottle of mineral water, added ice and poured a glass for her.

He's done this a thousand times before, she thought. But it was still a good show.

Jay was treating her as he would a date instead of an employee, and Abby was inclined to let him continue. An attentive, handsome escort was all part of her fantasy evening, and as long as she remembered that this wasn't a real date, she'd be fine. Besides, while Jay was flirting with her, he wouldn't get into trouble with anyone else and wasn't that the purpose of her going tonight?

So Abby smiled at Jay, drank her mineral water and scoured her mind for something brilliant to say. Or even any topic they could discuss. She'd grown up in a different world than the Lairds, but Jay turned out to be such an excellent conversationalist, Abby's lack of life experience didn't bother her.

"How about Dixieland Jazz? Ever been to New Orleans?" he asked.

Travel. Abby wanted to travel. Desperately. "No. But you have, I'll bet."

Jay nodded and finished pouring a drink for himself.

"For Mardi Gras?"

"Ah, Mardi Gras." Jay settled back, a reminiscent smile on his face. "What a party."

"Oh, tell me about it!"

Jay raised an eyebrow. "Well...I hooked up with one of the krewes and we built a float for the parade..."

When Jay finished telling her about Mardi Gras, he told her another of his travel adventures, and then another. Abby soaked them all in. Someday, she promised herself fiercely, she'd have stories of her own.

In the meantime, Jay's had to suffice. Abby only hoped all her questions didn't annoy him, or worse, bore him. She didn't want him escaping when they arrived at the hotel on the University of Houston campus.

"What itinerary would you suggest for a first-time European traveler?" Abby asked as they entered the campus proper.

"Well, London, naturally, and everyone should see Paris," Jay told her just as the car pulled to a stop. "But not in the summer when all the tourists are there," he was saying as the driver opened the door and he got out.

"But *I'd* be a tourist." Abby laughed. "And I think I'd be more comfortable mixing with the other tourists rather than wandering around all by myself." She scooted across the seat and took Jay's hand as she swung her legs out.

Abby had hoped for an elegant exit, but climbing out of a limo in a narrow skirt was a skill that required practice.

"You wouldn't be alone for long," Jay murmured as Abby surreptitiously smoothed her skirt.

The look he gave her was so frankly admiring that Abby's heart thudded in spite of reminding herself that Jay was just being Jay and she shouldn't take anything personally.

But still.

Jay kept hold of her hand and as they approached the glass doors, Abby saw her sparkling reflection and the handsome man next to her. She really was living a fairy tale and, thanks to Parker, she looked the part.

His thoughtful insistence on providing her with the

right dress for tonight was another example of his attention to details others might consider not worth their time.

Abby felt she would be learning a lot from working directly with Parker and vowed to absorb everything she could.

Before she and Jay reached the door, a woman dressed all in black crouched in front of them and took their picture. Her camera equipment was large enough so that Abby knew she was a professional photographer.

''Is she Lisa's replacement?'' the photographer called.

Jay waved her off with a smile, but under his breath Abby heard him murmur, ''Sorry about that.''

But Abby didn't mind. According to the office grapevine, Lisa had been very close to becoming Mrs. Jay Laird. Abby was secretly thrilled that she could be mistaken for his latest romantic interest. Wouldn't it be something if her picture actually made it into the society pages?

Feeling more confident, Abby floated into the reception. As the crowd thronged around him, Jay kept her close by. Since she was supposed to be watching him, this suited Abby just fine.

She found that all she had to do was smile and nod. Most of the conversations were the same, with people approaching Jay, dismayed that he was leaving and wanting to hear all about El Bahar. Sometimes he introduced her and sometimes he didn't. Abby didn't flatter herself that anyone would remember who she was. Or that they cared. It was enough that she was there.

As she watched the parade of women in blue, Abby

was very glad she'd chosen this dress and not the proper, but unexciting midnight-blue chiffon.

And then she heard a familiar voice. ''Hello, Jay. Abby, what did you get on that final exam?''

The crowd parted as Diamond Don, sparkling nearly as much as she was, approached them.

''I got an 'A', Mr. Danvers.''

''Atta girl. Where's Parker?''

Since the news would be in the paper, Abby felt it was all right to tell. ''He had to fly to Louisiana this afternoon. There was a well fire.''

''I heard about that,'' he said.

''Nothing to worry about,'' Jay said to him. ''Big brother's got everything under control.'' Though he smiled when he spoke, Abby heard the resentful tone in his voice and was sure the other man did, as well.

She puzzled over it until she remembered telling him that Parker had gone to Louisiana. He hadn't known anything about it. Diamond Don Danvers had known about the fire, but Jay hadn't.

When Jay turned to greet another acquaintance, Diamond Don leaned close to her ear. ''You keeping an eye on young Jay?''

''I'm representing Laird Drilling for Parker tonight,'' Abby said, not willing to confirm anything.

''Hmm.'' Diamond Don pulled a cigar out of his breast pocket and snipped off the end. ''Parker didn't see you in that pretty dress, did he?''

Abby found herself wishing he had. ''No, sir.''

Diamond Don chuckled. ''I didn't think so.'' Still smiling, he stuck the cigar in his mouth. ''You have a good time tonight, y'hear?'' Patting her arm, he wandered off, muttering, ''Gotta find where they've stuck the smokers this time.''

Although Diamond Don was the only person Abby

recognized, the rest of the evening was every bit as wonderful as she'd hoped. Jay, any sign of pique gone, snagged two glasses of champagne from a passing waiter and pressed one into her hand.

Champagne, and it wasn't even New Year's Eve. Even allowing herself this one glass, she felt positively decadent.

Jay touched her glass with his. "What would you like to drink to?" he asked, his mouth dangerously close.

"To magic," she said impulsively, and he smiled.

"Magic it is, then." Without taking his eyes from hers, he lifted the glass to his mouth.

He had a way of making them seem alone in the crowd. A way of making her feel self-aware in a way she wasn't used to.

Pretty heady stuff for a girl from Haste, Texas.

In a daze, Abby barely sipped at her champagne.

With a hand in the small of her back, Jay guided her to their blue-swathed table. "Hold this for me." He handed her his glass, then rearranged the silver place cards.

"Jay!" Abby looked around to see if anyone noticed. "You can't do that."

"Already done." He pulled out a chair. "You're now sitting next to me."

She allowed him to seat her. "But—"

"In spite of your disguise, they'll notice you aren't Parker," he murmured, bending near.

His breath raised gooseflesh on her arms and she felt something touch her neck.

If she hadn't known better, she would have sworn that it had been Jay's lips. But that was absolutely ridiculous. It was probably his lapel or shirt collar.

After dinner and a special presentation to Jay, the Jazz Ensemble played music for dancing.

Jay immediately stood and held out his hand. "Dance with me." He didn't give her the option to decline, not that she would have.

Abby melted into his arms as they swayed to the old-fashioned music. When she pulled back to talk with him, she noticed that his eyes were darker than his brother's. It made Jay's expression warmer somehow.

But then he pressed her against his shoulder and Abby didn't think about his eyes anymore.

This was absolutely better than her high school prom, the only other time she'd been to a formal dance.

Abby had expected to sit at a dinner table, watch Jay, and do her best to keep him on his best behavior. She hadn't expected the job to be so easy. He didn't seem to want to dance with anyone else and the only time Abby saw him even the slightest bit ruffled was when the woman society photographer kept flashing her camera at them.

As they danced, Abby leaned toward him and spoke directly into his ear. "Maybe if you smile, she'll get her picture and go away."

"They never go away." But Jay sent one of his grins toward the woman, who then popped off half a dozen shots before he turned his back and danced Abby into the crowd.

Abby couldn't believe she'd ever be ready for the evening to end, but at long last, even the weightless shoes began to feel heavy. And, she suspected that Jay had caught her trying to stifle a yawn.

"Ready to leave?" he asked, amusement audible in his voice.

Abby wanted to say no. She wanted the evening to last forever, the way it would in her memories.

"I know it's on the early side," Jay added, "but the movers are coming tomorrow at seven. *Seven a.m.* Can you believe it?"

Laughing at his expression, Abby shook her head. "Let's go then."

Looping her arm around his, he circled the room, saying his goodbyes and before she knew it, Abby was back in the limousine.

"You'll have to tell me where you live," Jay said.

"I live in an apartment on Westheimer, but my car is back at the Laird building."

"To the Laird building, James," Jay ordered the driver.

"Is his name really James?" Abby asked.

"No. It's Eugene. He prefers James."

Laughing softly at Jay's nonsense, Abby leaned her head back against the car seat. Turning to look at him, she said, "You've been awfully nice to me this evening. Thanks."

Jay's smile faded. "It's easy to be nice to you, Abby."

In the silence that followed, the car didn't seem quite so spacious. Incredibly, Abby thought Jay was about to kiss her, but inhaling sharply, he straightened and reached for the car phone.

"I'm going to make sure security is waiting for us. Do you need anything from the office?"

Abby thought about her purse and clothes, but decided she could get them tomorrow. "No. Just my car."

He was uncharacteristically silent until they'd located her car in the parking garage. "Thanks for giving up your evening, Abby."

Giving up a night eating popcorn and watching a rented video? She wanted to tell him how she'd dreamed about an evening such as this, but wisely settled for, "I had a wonderful time."

"So did I."

He spoke in a whisper as Eugene opened the door and she could barely make out the words. Garish fluorescent light flooded the interior of the car, signaling the end of her evening.

Jay and the driver waited until Abby had started her car, then followed her out of the parking garage. They turned in opposite directions.

"And the clock strikes twelve," Abby murmured, watching in the rearview mirror as the black car was swallowed up in the Houston night.

The Laird's New Lady?

Parker stared at the black and white photograph of his brother and some long-legged woman used to illustrate a story about the Jazz Ensemble dinner last night.

From one fire to another. Parker leaned his head against the car seat as Eugene drove him from the airport.

Parker sniffed. Turning his head he breathed close to the seat. Perfume. He smelled perfume. He'd bet Jay had that woman in the car with him last night.

And where, he wondered, had Abby been?

But immediately, he admitted he wasn't being fair. He shouldn't have expected so much of her. She was no match for Jay on the prowl.

Jay had probably laughed at him the entire evening.

Poor Abby. If Jay had insulted her...Parker swallowed as a surprising protectiveness surged through him.

He scanned the article, finding it just as offensive as he'd expected. He didn't recognize the woman and the reporters apparently hadn't, either. ''A beautiful newcomer to the Houston social scene,'' they described her.

The picture was of Jay and the woman dancing. He held her closely and his eyes were shut.

That was a very bad sign. If Jay's eyes were closed, he wasn't casing the room for another partner. And if he wasn't looking for another partner, it meant he was satisfied with the one he had.

Parker didn't want Jay to be satisfied. Parker wanted him lonely and depressed and ready to prove himself in El Bahar.

He shouldn't have gone to Louisiana.

Turning to the next page, Parker read the rest of the article. There was a picture of Jay accepting his plaque. There were other photographs of people who'd attended and though he studied them, Parker couldn't find a picture of Abby.

He had a appalling thought. ''Eugene?''

''Yes, Mr. Laird?''

''You drove my brother and Ms. Monroe to the dinner last night, didn't you?''

''Yes, Mr. Laird.''

''And you drove them home…at the same time?''

Eugene's eyes met his in the rearview. ''I dropped Ms. Monroe back at the Laird garage to retrieve her car.''

''And Jay?''

''I drove Mr. Jay directly home, sir.''

Alone? Parker wanted to ask, but didn't, finding continued questioning too demeaning. He'd find out soon enough, he supposed.

At least Abby had gone to the event, for all the good her presence had done.

"Eugene, take me directly to my brother's home."

"Yes, Mr. Laird."

With paper in hand, Parker arrived to find the movers already carting off crates of Jay's belongings. That was a relief, at least. He stood to one side as the base to Jay's heavy glass-topped dining table was carried out. If the glass survived the trip to El Bahar, he'd be surprised.

"Hey, there, Parker." Jay, looking more bright-eyed than Parker expected, set a box in a corner of his empty dining room. "Back so soon?"

"Um, yes." Parker had to mentally regroup. From the looks of the condo, Jay had been working with the movers for hours. "The fire was out when I got there."

"Gee, that's too bad," Jay said. "I know how you would have loved manning the hose yourself."

Parker eyed his brother. "I usually leave that to the professionals."

"Sure you trust them?"

"What's with you?" He followed Jay into his bedroom.

Jay shot him a look, then started picking through his compact disc collection. "The D-187A blows out, you take off for Louisiana, and I have to read the details in the newspaper."

Parker raked his fingers through his hair. It had been a long night. "Abby would have told you."

"Yes...Abby." Jay smiled in a way that set Parker's internal alarms clanging. "I suppose she told me what she knew." Plastic rattled as he chucked discs into a box on his bed. "Which wasn't much."

"I had to move fast," Parker explained without wanting to. "There wasn't time to brief you."

"But there was time to brief Don Danvers."

Parker rubbed at a spot between his eyebrows. "He's on the board."

"Well, what am I?"

Truthfully, it hadn't occurred to Parker to call Jay. He was accustomed to his brother's disinterest in the company and could have pointed that out, but chose to apologize instead. "I'm sorry. I should have let you know, but frankly, you couldn't have done anything anyway."

"How would you know?"

Why wouldn't his brother drop the subject? "What's the matter—did they pack your coffeepot already?"

Jay gestured with his head. "There's coffee in the kitchen, if you want. Of course it isn't ground and roasted to your specifications, but you may be able to swill it down."

Parker had indulged his brother's ill humor enough. "You were scheduled to receive an award." He held up the newspaper, picture folded out. "And you obviously recovered from my absence enough to have a wonderful time."

"Yeah. Abby's a sweet kid."

"Yes, she is. And I don't like the idea of you dumping her at a table somewhere while you dance with someone else!" Parker slapped the newspaper.

Jay glanced at the picture, then at his brother. "Had your eyes checked lately? That's Abby."

"What?" Parker stared at the photo. The woman's face was mostly obscured, but that wasn't Abby's hair. However, there was something about those legs... "It doesn't look like Abby."

''You're telling me.'' Jay tossed CDs into the box with a disregard that made Parker wince.

Obviously, Abby had turned out to be a better substitute for Valerie than he'd thought. *The Laird's New Lady*? No, but by the time the single women of Houston figured out Abby was just an employee, Jay would be in El Bahar.

This could work.

Parker breathed easier. Jay would be safe with Abby.

''I actually had fun last night,'' Jay admitted. ''The music was great. I think Abby is a jazz convert.''

''Maybe she'd enjoy hearing some of Dad's collection,'' Parker suggested. A small push couldn't hurt.

''Maybe.'' Jay shrugged. ''Look. Next time just tell me what's going on, okay? It's insulting when I don't know.''

''Okay,'' Parker agreed, wondering how long Jay's interest would last.

''So, hey—are you going to stand there or help me pack?''

Parker thought of the work waiting for him back at the office. ''Help you pack.''

CHAPTER SIX

ABBY changed the colored file folders on Parker's desk, putting the red one in the center, took a step back and exhaled. She was finally caught up. Of course being caught up would last only until Parker returned from Louisiana. But for now, it was a satisfying feeling.

She left his office, turned off her computer and picked up the society section of the morning newspaper where she gazed at her picture for the twentieth time. She'd be barely recognizable to her friends and family, but Abby was thrilled all the same.

She'd bought three copies of the newspaper so she could send a clipping to her parents. There she was—dancing with the guest of honor at a gathering of Houston's elite. Her parents would never believe it. *She* barely believed it.

Maybe she should buy more copies.

She and Jay weren't the only ones to be pictured in the newspaper. Parker, wearing a hard hat, appeared in the business section under the ominous headline, Laird CEO Assesses Damage.

It didn't sound good, though in the body of the article Parker sounded upbeat. Canned, but upbeat. Abby had clipped the article and put it in the yellow information folder.

She had not put in a clipping from the jazz party last night.

Abby was preparing to leave for lunch, when a dark

blur raced past the outside office. After a moment, it returned and Parker materialized in the doorway.

But it was a different Parker. One who wore jeans, a knit shirt and running shoes. And was that a dirt smudge on his shoulder?

"Hi, Abby, how did it go last night?"

She stared, thrown by the sight of Parker in casual clothes. "Fine."

He blinked and seemed to be waiting for her to elaborate. What could she tell him? He'd hardly be interested in her fairy-tale fantasies, but that's what the evening had been to her—a real-life fantasy.

"Jay received a really nice plaque. Um, everybody there said they were sorry he was leaving. We, uh, danced..."

"I saw the picture." Something flickered in his eyes and a corner of his mouth rose. "I didn't recognize you."

Abby felt her face grow warm. "Even I didn't recognize me!"

His face creased into a full smile. "I assume Neiman's took care of you then."

"T-the dress was beautiful." And no doubt hideously expensive. "Thanks."

He raised his hand in a negligent gesture. "Enjoy it. You've earned it. Did the saleswoman remember the gift certificates?"

"What gift certificates?" Abby didn't have a clue as to what he was talking about.

"I ordered them for Barbara and Nancy. I know you all have to pick up the slack with Valerie gone."

"What a lovely gesture." Abby knew there were small extras given to the staff from time to time, but she'd assumed they'd always come from Valerie. At least that was the impression Valerie gave. Now Abby wondered.

Parker looked uncomfortable. "I wanted them—and you—to know I appreciate their efforts."

And she hadn't even looked at the bill. "I put the envelope with the receipt on your desk." At the time, she thought it had seemed awfully thick.

"I'll check there." He started to leave.

"Parker?"

"Yes?"

She'd started to tell him how giving Barbara and Nancy the gift certificates at the same time he'd bought her a dress had made her feel more comfortable, but changed her mind. It didn't seem right to mention it, so she said, "I was leaving for lunch, unless you need me for anything?"

He had blank look on his face and Abby realized he'd already dismissed her and turned his thoughts elsewhere. Typical. The man was amazing that way. He concentrated completely on something and when he was finished, he just as completely wiped it from his mind.

"Oh. No. See you this afternoon."

Parker absently rubbed his shoulder while he looked through the files Abby had set on his desk. He'd strained his shoulder hefting boxes Jay didn't trust to the movers. About now, Jay would be discovering how heavy those boxes were as he unloaded the pickup truck he'd borrowed from a friend.

Parker stopped reading and rubbed his eyes. He needed a break. Maybe he would ease up after Jay went to El Bahar. Maybe he'd even take an entire weekend off and...do something. Something else.

Something he'd figure out when he had the time.

Grimacing, Parker came to the article about the well fire. Hard hats made his head look like a mushroom.

The article could have been worse. When he'd arrived at the well, he could tell the local press had been hoping for more of a disaster. A major environmental catastrophe would draw the national media and shine the limelight on the local reporters. But Peter had been right—the fire was out and cleanup had already begun. Still, any problems involving Laird Drilling this close to beginning the El Bahar joint venture would be noted by the El Baharis.

One more week. One more week and the deal would be finalized and Jay would be in charge of his first major project.

One more week and Parker could relax.

On Wednesday morning, Parker stepped off the elevator, automatically glanced toward the staff offices, which were empty, and toward Valerie's, which wasn't. "Good morning, Abby," he called to the beige figure he saw behind the frosted glass.

"Good morning, Parker," he heard in response.

With his customary pace, he was halfway down the hall before registering that *two* voices had responded to his greeting.

Veering into the conference room, he cut back toward his assistant's office.

"Now tell me what the pink one is for again?" he heard a laughing bass voice ask.

He knew that voice. "Jay? What are you doing here?"

Parker reached the doorway to find his brother standing over Abby, who was seated at her desk.

"I...work here?" Jay grinned.

Uneasily, Parker noted Abby's laughing expression, bright eyes and the attractive peachy flush that stained her cheeks.

His mind flashed to the picture of the leggy woman dancing with Jay on Monday night.

"It's not even eight o'clock in the morning," was all Parker could say.

"Yes, and where have you been?"

"I—I just got here." Parker was rattled. He wasn't used to being rattled. He didn't like being rattled.

"Well, hurry up. We're just about ready to discuss your schedule, aren't we, Abby?"

She nodded after darting glances from Jay to Parker.

"*We*?"

"Abby is teaching me the ins and outs of being your assistant. I figured that I'll have to set up my own routine in El Bahar and I thought, why not learn yours?"

Jay's reasoning sounded very logical, which further alarmed Parker. Jay was not known for his logic. On the other hand, his remark about El Bahar encouraged Parker to think that Jay might be taking his new position more seriously.

"Fine." Parker smiled benignly at them both, grabbed a cup of coffee, and proceeded to his office, only to stare at his clean desktop. He'd left instructions for Abby, and she was presumably acting on those instructions.

Muted laughter resonated through the open door of the conference room.

Jay. Jay was in there distracting Abby and upsetting Parker's routine. Irritated, he buzzed her. "Is the schedule ready, yet?"

"We'll be right in."

Parker waited, bouncing the eraser end of a pencil. Normally, the day's preliminary schedule was waiting for him on his desk. Even though he knew his trip to Louisiana had caused changes, he found himself annoyed.

It was the laughing, he realized, catching sight of his brother and Abby making their way through the conference room. Parker was used to quiet.

They reached the open doorway and Jay gestured Abby in with an elaborate bow. Giggling, she passed by him.

Something twisted in the vicinity of Parker's heart.

Abby approached the desk while Jay dragged a chair over. Parker ignored the tracks it made in the rug.

"So every morning starts with a schedule conference, right?" Jay positioned his chair close to Abby's and leaned over to look at the book she'd opened.

"Yes." Parker and Abby answered at the same time.

Jay gave a low whistle. "Man, you've got something every fifteen minutes."

"Today is busier than usual," Abby said. "I have to reschedule the appointments Parker missed because of the Louisiana trip." She looked at him. "I have calls in, but it's still early to reach everyone."

Parker nodded. "It's important to keep your assistant informed, so she can have some independence in adjusting your schedule should the need arise." An overwhelming feeling of déjà vu assaulted Parker. His father might have said those very words to him. In fact, Parker could hear their echo now.

He was also aware of the look Jay exchanged with Abby and the telltale quiver at the corner of her mouth.

Parker knew he sounded stuffy and made an effort to loosen up during the next half hour.

To his credit, Jay paid attention, though he didn't take notes and Parker decided he wouldn't suggest Jay do so. Let him learn what happened when you didn't watch the details.

"You don't have dinner on there." Jay pointed to Abby's book.

"Dinner?" Parker asked.

"You promised Mother you'd have dinner with us tonight and I will chain myself to your leg if you try to back out." Jay looked as stern as Parker had ever seen him.

"Dinner at eight," Parker directed Abby.

"Six," corrected Jay.

"Six is impossible with the traffic."

"Seven, then," Jay said through gritted teeth.

The brothers glared at each other.

"Abby, dinner at my mother's is etched in stone, got that?" Jay said.

"I'll *try* to be there," Parker said heavily. "I might be late—"

"Abby, I'm inviting you to dinner with my mother tonight. Would you like to come?"

"I, uh..." Poor Abby was looking from him to Jay.

"We'll listen to the old jazz records I promised you. Bring a date." He snapped his fingers. "May I suggest Parker? Seven o'clock. Don't be late."

Abby assumed Jay had been teasing, but at five forty-five, Eugene appeared at the door to her office. "We need to leave now, Ms. Monroe. Mr. Laird is way out on the Katy Freeway and we'll hit the thick of the traffic."

"You go on, Eugene. Good night."

The driver hesitated. ''Are you driving yourself to Ms. Laird's, ma'am?''

She smiled at him. ''Oh, I'm not going.''

''I have my instructions, ma'am. Mr. Jay said I was to make sure you got Mr. Laird out of his meeting and to have you both at his mother's by seven.'' Eugene pointedly checked his watch.

That did it. The temptation to be part of a Laird family dinner was too much to resist. After all, Abby *had* been invited. And she'd get to ride in the limousine again.

Quickly gathering her notebook and the latest schedule, she followed Eugene into the elevator.

Getting stuck in traffic had never been so comfortable, Abby thought fifteen minutes later. She enjoyed her ride in the luxurious car so much, she was almost able to forget the fact that she would soon be having an intimate dinner with Parker, Jay and their mother.

Her hands turned to ice. What would they talk about? Just how deep could she mine travel as a conversation topic? Business? Would they discuss business? Until recently, Abby hadn't been privy to any top-level business.

Maybe she should insist on returning to the Laird building. Maybe—

The car phone rang.

Abby jumped. Should she answer it? Of course she should. ''Mr. Laird's car,'' she said.

A burst of laughter sounded in her ear. ''Oh, Abby, you're a doll. Where are you?''

It was Jay. Just hearing his voice made her breathe easier. ''On the Katy Freeway. We don't have Parker yet.''

He groaned. ''You'll never make it to The

Woodlands by seven. Ditch Parker and tell Eugene to bring you on.''

Abby blinked. ''I can't do that.''

Jay lowered his voice. ''I suppose not, but I wish you would.''

He's just flirting with you. He flirts with everyone. Still, it was beginning to make her slightly uncomfortable.

In the end, she did have to drag Parker from the meeting. Introducing herself to her counterpart at Northwest Drilling Supply, Abby and the other woman entered the office where Parker and two men were engaged in a heated debate.

''I don't dispute the cost increase, but twelve percent?'' Parker had actually raised his voice.

He still looked cool and elegant in the dark suit and crisp white shirt compared to the brown sport coats the other men wore, but it was obvious that he was on the verge of losing his temper. She didn't know Parker had a temper to lose.

''Well, now, Parker, you can go shopping and you can probably do better, but you won't do quicker.'' A man with a shock of white hair grinned.

Parker glanced toward Abby, then scooped up the papers surrounding him and whisked them into his briefcase in one movement. Snapping the clasps shut, he stood. ''Four percent.''

The man cackled. ''You're asking us to *give* 'em to you.''

''Four percent,'' Parker repeated. ''Think it over and if you agree to my offer, fax me a preliminary contract by tomorrow at nine.'' He offered his hand. ''I hope we can continue to do business.''

The men remained seated. ''Now, hold on, Parker. Sit yourself back down and let's talk about this.''

"I have another appointment, gentlemen."

Abby saw that he really was going to leave and backed out of the small office. She wished she hadn't had to interrupt the meeting. She probably shouldn't have.

Within seconds, Parker strode toward her. "I'm not going to yell at you, so quit looking as though I am," he said under his breath as he passed her.

Abby had to hurry to keep up. "I'm sorry. I felt uncomfortable interrupting you." And horrified that he'd noticed her discomfort. If Parker had noticed, so had the others.

"Keeping me on schedule is your job." He held open the building door for her. "In this case, I knew you were coming and planned to make my final offer before walking out. Give them overnight to think about it."

Eugene opened the car door and Abby climbed in, this time sitting in the seat facing the rear so Parker could have access to the telephone and computer.

He pulled down a walnut ledge that acted as a small worktable. "Northwest thinks they can charge whatever they want and I'll have to pay it. I want to meet with Elkins in Purchasing tomorrow at eight-thirty." Parker, in the middle of setting up the computer, glanced at her. "Aren't you writing this down?"

"Oh!" Abby grabbed her notebook. Here was another of her fantasies: working in a limo, though, quite frankly, she found the motion of the car distracting.

Parker continued dictating instructions just as though they were in the office. As usual, he worked at an impossible pace and Abby enjoyed her part in it. She'd never look at a limousine in the same way, though. Jay might use the car to impress women, but to Parker it was a mobile office.

He made several phone calls and Abby gazed out the window, pretending she didn't hear. He was very different from Jay and she couldn't help contrasting her two experiences in the car. She tried to imagine Parker flirting and couldn't, so she imagined him as Jay only looking like Parker.

The result made her catch her breath. A man who looked like Parker and flirted like Jay would be irresistible. Her heart had actually picked up speed at the thought. She imagined dancing with Parker, of being held as closely by him as Jay had held her, and an unnerving tension washed over her.

To dispel it, she recalled lectures from her "Strategies for Women in Business" course—specifically the part about business socializing.

Monday night and dinner tonight were business. She was only here because Valerie wasn't. Though dinner was at the Laird home, this was a business function and Abby should treat it as such. If she started daydreaming about fancy evenings with her boss and his brother, she was going to be very disappointed when Valerie returned, sending Abby back to her regular position on the staff.

Her regular position on the staff. It was the first time Abby had considered life after Valerie returned, and she knew she'd never again be satisfied with typing productions at her desk by the elevator. And if she did a good job for Parker, no, a *fabulous* job, maybe she wouldn't have to.

"We're nearly there," Parker said as they turned off the highway. Looking at his watch, he gave a lopsided grimace. "We're late."

"N-not by much," Abby said, still jolted by her thoughts.

Parker closed his computer. "Are you all right?"

''I'm a little nervous,'' Abby confessed, which was true.

He didn't ask her why and she was glad.

''No need to be nervous. We give the butler and footmen Wednesdays off.''

Abby's eyes widened.

''I'm joking,'' he murmured, and clicked the shelf back into place.

''So it's not their night off?''

Parker gave her a look. ''I was joking about having a butler and footmen.''

''Oh,'' she said in a small voice. Since flinging herself out of a moving car wasn't an attractive option, she turned to stare out the window.

''Just remember that Jay invited us to be a distraction for my mother. They...have similar personalities.''

''And they don't get along?'' Abby still couldn't meet Parker's gray gaze.

''It's more that they exhaust each other.''

What an odd comment. Now she did face him.

He smiled faintly. ''You'll see.''

Jay greeted them with effusive relief. Mrs. Laird was equally welcoming, in a gracious, smothering way. She was a tall woman—taller than Abby—and both her sons resembled her, though perhaps Jay more than Parker.

Mrs. Laird drew Abby through the foyer into a two-story den with a white marble fireplace, keeping up a constant stream of social chatter, which Jay supplemented whenever his mother paused for breath. As she had on Monday night, Abby found that all she had to do was smile and nod, or respond to an occasional direct question, and let Jay and his mother carry the conversational ball.

Once, Abby caught Parker's eye, and they shared a look of understanding. No wonder he was the silent type, she thought. How could he be anything else?

But since Abby was also more of a listener than a talker, she didn't mind the chatter and enjoyed listening to the jazz records after dinner.

Each number prompted a story from Mrs. Laird, usually involving where she and her husband had been when they first heard the song. During one anecdote, Abby looked to see Parker's and Jay's reactions and was intrigued by their expressions. Surprisingly, Jay's face was closed and Abby imagined him gritting his teeth, but Parker wore a yearning look that told her how much he'd admired his father.

It was easy to see that Jay got along better with their mother and Parker had identified more with their father. Abby didn't know exactly what the significance was, but for her, just knowing—even just being here tonight—made her feel like an insider.

And she realized she never wanted to go back to being an outsider.

Parker felt a familiar dullness begin behind his eyes and spread to his temples. He found extended doses of both his mother and Jay draining.

He wondered what Abby was thinking. She sat quietly and listened with apparent interest to his mother's stories. Jay's incessant babbling didn't appear to bother her, either. In fact, she seemed to encourage him.

Abby was a restful sort of person. Even Jay seemed calmer. He perched on the arm of her overstuffed chair and frequently murmured in her ear, making her blush at whatever he said.

Shifting on the couch, Parker gritted his teeth.

Didn't Jay ever give it a rest? If Abby weren't so levelheaded, he'd be worried that she might read more into Jay's attention than she should. But, he was grateful Jay was here and content to entertain Abby, and not hanging around with his usual crowd. Perhaps his little brother was growing up at last.

Though it was ten-thirty and they were forty-five minutes from home, Jay showed no sign of ending the evening. It was obviously going to fall to Parker, so when the next record finished, he stood. "It's time we headed back." He was gratified to see that Abby also stood. "Will we see you tomorrow, Jay?"

Jay's eyes met his in a look Parker couldn't quite define. "You can count on it."

On Thursday morning, to Parker's astonishment, Jay was once again at work, waving at him from Barbara and Nancy's office. Abby was also in the room and they all looked as though they were having a grand old time.

Parker nodded stiffly and continued on to his office, a burst of laughter following him down the hall.

Jay spent the morning with Abby, and, miraculously, she still managed to keep up with her work for Parker as well as help Jay set up his own office routine. She was obviously capable of more than the junior position on his support staff. Parker made a mental note to see about giving her more responsibility when Valerie returned.

He stopped by her office at noon. "Abby, I'm leaving now."

She consulted his schedule. "For your lunch with the Northwestern Drilling board?"

"Yes."

"Good old Northwestern must have decided a four-percent increase isn't so bad after all,'' Jay said. ''Let me know how it goes. I'll be in the market for drilling pipe pretty quick here.''

Golden words. Miraculous words. Words Parker had hoped to hear from his brother someday. He smiled, but Jay was looking at Abby and missed it.

''And don't worry, I'll feed Abby lunch,'' he said.

Actually, Parker hadn't been concerned about feeding Abby at all. ''She can call out for something if she wants to.''

''Parker, Parker, Parker.'' Stretching, Jay came to his feet with a languid movement that made Parker straighten his own shoulders. ''She's been working too hard. She needs a break. Can't I interest you in some lunch, Abby?''

''Oh...'' Abby looked at him before answering Jay. ''That's not necessary. I can grab a sandwich from downstairs.''

''Go if you want to,'' Parker said. ''I don't mind.''

But, inexplicably, he did.

For years he'd seen his brother turn on a heated charm that melted women. Even Abby blushed and smiled. But Abby knew Jay was leaving soon, and while she might be flattered to be treated to a lunch out, she knew better than to take his brother seriously.

''Abby, I need you in my office!'' Parker roared as soon as he got off the elevator after lunch.

Abby hurried after him. ''This just came in, Parker.'' She handed him a fax from Northwestern Drilling Supply.

''I already know what it says and I will *not* pay an eleven percent increase.'' Jaw tight, Parker thought for a moment. ''I'm going to have to visit alternate suppliers. Immediately.''

"Do you know which ones, or shall I check the files?" Abby asked.

"Get me the file with recent bid correspondence and tell Elkins in Purchasing I need to see him right away."

Abby literally ran out the door, rushing past Jay with a hurried greeting. Jay, hands in his pockets, turned to watch her. "So what's going on?"

By the time Parker filled him in, Abby was back. "I've got to leave today in order to get back here by the board meeting Friday morning." He leveled a look at his brother. "This means you'll have to complete the El Bahar report to the Board on your own."

Jay made a circle with his thumb and index finger. "No problemo." A smile creased his face and he draped an arm around Abby's shoulders. "Abby will keep me in line. Won't you, Abby?"

"I'll do my best," she said with a shy smile.

"See?" Jay grinned at him. "Nothing to worry about."

CHAPTER SEVEN

FRIDAY morning, Parker stepped off the elevator and headed for his office. When he passed the conference room, he saw Jay pacing and released the breath he hadn't realized he was holding. His brother was here in time for the meeting. Good. Great. Better than great.

"Parker!" Jay ran after him.

"Hi. Did you get the report finished?" Parker didn't want to ask, but he had to know.

"Yeah. Sure. Listen—"

"Great. El Bahar is your baby." Parker flung his briefcase on the sofa and tore off his jacket. He'd cut his arrival back in Houston too close, but in the end, he'd found another pipe supplier, so the trip had paid off.

"Well, see, I wanted to talk with you about that."

"What? You want to run part of the report by me now? Better make it quick. We don't have much time."

"I think I'm in love with Abby," Jay announced baldly.

Parker stopped in the act of yanking off his tie and stared at his brother. Abby? Love? Jay thought he was in love with *Abby*? Parker felt like he'd been kicked in the head. Jay wasn't supposed to be in love with anybody—especially not Abby.

Wearing a nervously defiant expression, Jay stood just inside the door of Parker's office suite.

Parker schooled his own features as he finished removing his tie and started unbuttoning his shirt. *Downplay. Don't overreact. Don't react at all.* ''And?''

''And?'' Jay came farther into the room. ''*And*? Is that all you have to say? I just told you I'm in love with Abby.''

''You said you *thought* you were in love with Abby.'' Parker jerked at the buttons of his shirt. ''You've thought you were in love with a lot of women. Lisa comes to mind.''

Jay blinked once, then turned to study the watercolors of drilling sites that lined Parker's walls. ''This is different.''

Yes, it was. Months of negotiations with the wary El Baharis were on the line. ''You hardly know Abby.'' As soon as he said the words, Parker regretted them.

Sure enough, Jay took the opening Parker had given him. ''Well, that's what we need to talk about. I want time to get to know Abby better.''

Parker tried stalling. ''I've been up all night. I came to the office straight from the airport and the board meeting is in an hour. I've got to take a shower. We'll talk after the meeting.''

''No!''

Parker raised an eyebrow and unbuckled his belt.

''If we don't talk now, we'll talk in front of the board.''

Of all the times for his brother to stand up to him. ''Fine. I'm still taking a shower.'' Parker stripped off his pants and headed to the bathroom. He felt cold—colder than he'd ever remembered feeling.

''Don't brush me off, Parker!'' Jay stormed after him.

''Suit yourself.''

"Abby is the woman I've been looking for all my life," Jay declared with his usual dramatic style.

Parker opened the faucet and stepped into the shower. Though he turned up the hot water, he couldn't get warm. The thing of it was, Abby probably *was* good for Jay. She had an appealing sweetness about her without being a pushover. She was intelligent and lacked the cynicism so prevalent in Jay's crowd. Their mother had liked her. Parker knew she was ambitious and willing to work hard. In fact—

"Now that I've found Abby...I—I can't just leave for a year. Or longer."

There it was: Jay backing out. Quitting. Again. The hot water beat on Parker's shoulders. Abby. Jay wasn't supposed to fall in love with Abby. Abby wasn't his type. Lisa was his type. But was he really in love? Or was he using Abby as an excuse to get out of going to El Bahar? Anger, frustration and an emotion he couldn't define warred within Parker. Jay had begged for responsibility. A chance, he'd said. So Parker had given him one. A big one. A real one. "What does Abby say?"

There was a silence before Jay admitted, "I haven't told her how I feel yet."

"So you don't even know if she feels the same way?" Hope warmed him. Jay continued talking. Parker lifted his head out of the water spray and concentrated on his brother's words.

"I think she has feelings for me," Jay said with a confidence that no doubt came from experience. "She just doesn't know it yet."

Parker thought of the picture in the society section of the newspaper, Abby's blushes and the shared laughter. He grabbed the soap and started scrubbing as though he could scrub away his thoughts. Did Abby feel the same way about Jay?

She couldn't. Parker refused to believe that the levelheaded Abby Monroe he'd come to know would be swayed by his brother.

But Jay could hurt her if she *did* fall in love with him.

The realization disturbed Parker. He didn't for a moment believe Jay's feelings ran any deeper than a glass of water. Jay didn't know what he wanted or what he felt. He was as immature as ever. Jay probably expected *Parker* to explain his "feelings" to the board.

And Parker vowed he would not.

Jay leaned against the tiled wall. "There's something so *fresh* about Abby. She's different from anybody I've ever met before. Everything is still new and exciting to her."

And Parker had thought Abby's unsophistication would be a turnoff to Jay. Man, he'd been way off base.

"She's not bored by life. And when I'm with her, I'm not bored, either."

"You won't have time to be bored in El Bahar," Parker threw out, though he suspected it wouldn't do any good. In the next half hour, he was going to have to convince Jay that he wasn't in love with Abby and that he should go to El Bahar as scheduled.

"It's more than not being bored. She—she looks up to me. She makes me feel smart and important."

If you want to feel smart and important, get a dog. Parker barely refrained from suggesting it. "She wouldn't think it very smart of you to give up this opportunity to run an entire division of the company, would she?"

"I'm not giving it up...I just don't want to leave next week." He laughed. "All that oil isn't going anywhere."

All that oil...! Parker squeezed the washcloth until every drop of water was wrung from it. "We've signed an agreement with the government of El Bahar saying that we would begin operations next week."

"Well, that Ian what's-his-name you hired will be there, won't he? I can call him on the phone."

"You can't run an operation that way!" Parker flung the wadded up washcloth at the shower wall.

"Because *you* never have?"

"Jay, you're not being realistic. You have months of intense, *hands-on* work ahead of you."

"I know, I know. But my relationship with Abby—"

"You don't *have* a relationship with Abby!" Parker turned off the shower and grabbed a towel.

"And I'll never have one if I'm stuck in the desert." Jay's voice was loud in the now-quiet bathroom.

Parker toweled himself dry and tried to think. "So what you're saying is that you expect to walk into the board meeting and tell them, 'Sorry folks, it's all off'?" Tying the towel around his waist, he stepped from the stall and met his brother's stubborn gaze. There was no tentativeness about him. Obviously, Jay had been stewing about this for a while.

"Not off." He lifted a shoulder. "Maybe postponed a couple of months—I don't know."

"A couple of months." Parker glared at him. "Is that how long it will take you to lose interest in her?"

"You don't understand! Abby's...special." His eyes lit up in a way that gave Parker a sinking feeling in his stomach. "You know she wants to travel?"

Parker shook his head.

"I want to show her London, Paris and Rome. I want to take her on a gondola ride in Venice. I want to explore German castles with her. I want to feed her Sacher torte in Austria. Bicycle through Provence—"

"I get the idea," Parker interrupted.

Jay came back to earth. "I'm in this for the long haul," he vowed.

"And then what?" Parker turned to the mirror and wondered if he should risk shaving. With the mood he was in, he'd probably slice off his upper lip. "In two months, you'll tell me you can't go to El Bahar because you don't want to be away from her that long."

"That might happen."

No shaving. "What's more likely to happen is that after a couple of weeks Abby's 'freshness' will get stale. Her wide-eyed wonder will get on your nerves." Parker pushed past Jay, grabbed underwear and socks from the bureau and headed for the closet. "You'll get bored and you'll drop her for the first blonde who walks by!"

"I won't. Haven't you been listening to me?" Jay followed him and sat on the arm of the couch.

"I've seen you do it before." Why couldn't he sit on the chair seat like everyone else? Parker selected a suit and stepped into the pants.

"This time is different."

"So you've said." He thrust his arms into a shirt.

"Oh, I get it." Jay's mouth twisted. "Just because I won't sacrifice my life and happiness on the altar of business the way you have, you won't take me seriously."

Parker's hold on his temper slipped. "You don't *deserve* to be taken seriously! You have a responsibility to this company, to those investors—" his cuffs flapped as he pointed toward the conference room "—and to me! And you want to walk away from it all for a girl you've known a few days."

"She's not just any girl—"

"That's right. She's our employee. *Employee*, Jay. The rules are different."

From the look on Jay's face, Parker could tell he hadn't considered that aspect.

There was *his* opening. Parker drew a calming breath and finished buttoning his shirt. "You need to be very careful. And before you make any irrevocable decisions, you should know how Abby feels. She might be engaged to the boy back home, for all you know."

Jay's startled look couldn't have been faked. He must really like her, Parker thought. But Jay always fell in love quickly. The problem was, he never fell very far.

"I—I guess you're right."

Parker moved to the mirror and knotted his tie. "Tell you what. The board needs to hear the report and approve the final draft of the budget. The basic facts won't change no matter who is in charge. Go ahead and make the presentation. It'll buy time and we'll talk more afterwards."

"Yeah. Okay." Jay was subdued.

He stood and Parker clapped him on the shoulder. "You're good at selling, Jay. People like listening to you talk."

Jay gave him a look. "Consolation time, right? After annihilating your opponent, you throw him a few minor concessions so he won't feel so bad?"

Parker slid his arm down. "I'm telling you the truth. You're better with people than I am. They like you. You always know what to say and how to say it.'' He gestured awkwardly. ''I'm...not as effective with people.''

''Is the great Parker Laird admitting that his little brother is actually *better* at something than he is?''

Parker smiled. ''Don't get cocky, kid.''

Abby finished brewing coffee for the meeting, following Parker's instructions exactly. She wanted no repeat of Monday's humiliating episode.

Except—it hadn't been humiliating, thanks to Parker. Covering for her had been sweet of him and sweet wasn't a word one associated with Parker Laird.

Or it hadn't been until Abby started working directly with him. She was learning that Parker Laird was a complex man who was difficult—but not impossible—to get to know.

And then there was Jay, as open as Parker was closed. Abby smiled and arranged the mugs. She liked Jay, but he was easy to like, with his constant flattery and joking. He was also exhausting. Again she smiled, remembering Parker's description of his mother and Jay. Exhausting was exactly the right word.

She heard murmurs and then, ''Abby!''

Jay, a broad grin on his face, strode into the conference room from Parker's office. ''Going to listen to me give my presentation?''

Automatically, Abby glanced toward the dark-haired man who followed Jay and was taken aback by the intensity of his gray eyes. ''I—I've already heard it twice.''

''But that was just practice. This is for real.''

''Abby has her own work to do, Jay,'' Parker said repressively.

Shoving his hands into his pockets, Jay turned to Parker. ''Let her stay—for luck.''

Though he spoke lightly, the way he and Parker locked gazes told Abby something else was going on here and for some unfathomable reason, whether or not she stayed in the room was important.

Great. She was caught in the middle of a sibling argument, but Parker was her boss. "I am pretty busy, Jay." She smiled encouragingly. "You'll do fine."

"Thanks to your help," Jay said. "Abby stayed after work to help me put the report together," he told Parker. "I don't know what I would have done without her."

Abby felt her cheeks heat as Parker's eyes turned toward her once more.

"I have no objection to you sitting in on the meeting." But his tone said otherwise.

"Great!" Jay was smiling again.

Parker wasn't.

"Sit here, Abby." Jay dragged a chair from her careful arrangement around the table.

"No, Jay," she said, and replaced the chair. "I'll stand just inside the door so I can slip out if I need to."

At that moment, Nancy ushered in the first arrivals, so Abby was spared any more of Jay's protests.

Parker was sure in a foul mood, she thought as she stationed herself by the coffee bar. His trip must have been unsuccessful.

Abby sighed inwardly. That meant another trip and she'd already rescheduled three meetings. Though it wasn't her fault, she felt guilty knowing that the secretaries she spoke to would now have to rearrange their boss's schedules yet again.

When Parker called the board meeting to order and turned the floor over to Jay, Abby walked quietly to the back of the room. Jay cleared his throat and she sent him an encouraging smile, then became aware of Parker's gaze.

He was watching her and not his brother. She raised her eyebrows in a question in case Parker wanted her for something, but he shook his head and turned to watch Jay.

During Jay's presentation, Parker studied Abby, analyzing her every smile and gesture. How *did* she feel about Jay? She laughed at his jokes, along with the rest of the board, and nodded a couple of times. Once, Jay winked at her, and she grinned. But love? Parker didn't think so—yet. It was the possibility that bothered him. With time short, Jay would turn up the charm. He'd dazzle her, and who knew how she'd react?

After another burst of laughter, Parker turned his full attention to Jay. His brother had a real talent for public speaking. What might have been a dry-as-sand budget report had become entertaining. Jay answered questions and allayed fears regarding his lack of experience. Jay's appointment had not been unanimously approved and at every board meeting, someone usually voiced concerns. Jay indicated that he planned to rely on Ian Douglass's know-how, which was a good tactic, since the board knew Ian.

By the end of Jay's presentation, Parker was more determined than ever that Jay should go to El Bahar. He could run that operation and run it well. Afterwards, his industry reputation would be well-established. If he gave up this opportunity, it would be years before the board would ever approve him for anything again.

"If there are no further questions, do I hear a motion to approve the first quarter operating budget?'' Parker asked.

''So moved!'' shouted Diamond Don.

The entire board seconded and amid the resulting laughter, Parker had a difficult time holding a formal vote for the record.

Afterwards, during the congratulations, he watched Jay search the room and realized he was looking for Abby. Parker knew the exact instant Jay caught her eye, because his face lit up and he grinned a sappy, mushy grin. He might as well broadcast his feelings to the world.

For her part, Abby gave him a thumbs-up and left the room.

Parker had to speak with her. He had to find out if Jay's feelings were completely one-sided. He started to follow, but Diamond Don waylaid him.

''It does my heart good to see your brother finally comin' aboard the company.''

''Yes,'' Parker agreed. ''And I appreciate the board's support of him.'' He edged away.

''Yeah, that took some arm twisting, but I see great things for the future of Laird Drilling.''

Parker turned back to the flamboyant, silver-haired oilman. Apparently, he owed more to Diamond Don's influence than he'd realized.

Diamond Don reached for a cigar. ''Jay seems real taken with little Abby. Now there's a gal who'll keep him in line.''

He'd noticed. He'd noticed Jay's interest in Abby and was warning Parker.

''Yes. She's a good worker.'' Parker came to a decision. If Diamond Don voiced an opinion, however veiled, it behooved him to listen. ''Don, I'm searching for a new pipe supplier and I'll be out of town for a few days. Since Abby will be with me,'' he paused and the two men exchanged a look of understanding, ''will you be available in case Jay has any last-minute questions?''

''Sure thing.'' Grinning, Diamond Don stuck the cigar in his mouth.

''You want me to come with you to where?'' Abby couldn't believe that moments after the meeting ended, Parker Laird was standing in her office telling her she was about to travel on Laird company business.

''Colombé,'' he repeated. ''It's a privately-owned island in the Eastern Caribbean. We'll be house guests of Kitt Ramsdell. I want his bid on the pipe before I decide on a new supplier.''

The Caribbean! Abby gripped the edge of her desk. ''H-how soon are we leaving?''

''How soon can you pack?''

Abby's eyes widened.

Parker held up a hand. ''Just pack the necessities. If you need something else we'll buy it there.''

All Abby could think about was the gaping elastic on her old swimsuit. She *knew* she should have hit the sales at the end of last season.

This is business, whispered the voice of reason. *You won't have time to play.* ''How long will we be on Colombé?'' she asked.

''Could be a day, but prepare for several days. Kitt won't be in a working mood.''

Abby grabbed her notebook. ''What arrangements shall I make?''

''Arrangements?'' Parker gazed blankly at her.

''For the trip,'' she prompted.

He'd been in a strange mood all morning. And the

way he kept staring at her... Even during Jay's presentation, he'd been preoccupied. Abby had stayed through the whole thing, though she hadn't planned to, but it was so obvious that Parker wasn't paying attention, she'd wanted to show Jay her support.

"Sorry," he mumbled. "I didn't get any sleep last night. You go on home and I'll take care of things on this end. Eugene will pick you up in an hour."

"I can't be ready in an hour!" While it sounded glamorous to drop everything and head for an island in the Caribbean, there were a few pesky details she couldn't ignore. "Maybe Valerie moved that fast, but I've got to talk with Nancy and Barbara, finish up here, drive home, get my neighbor to pick up the newspaper and my mail, pack—"

"Okay. We'll leave in two hours then."

"Where are we going?" a grinning Jay asked from the doorway. "Lunch, to celebrate?"

"No, to a meeting with Kitt Ramsdell."

Abby opened her mouth to congratulate Jay, but Parker ushered Jay out the door before she had a chance to say anything to him.

"I'm still chasing pipe. By the way, you did a great job with the presentation," Abby heard Parker say as they disappeared into the conference room.

This pipe issue must be more important than she realized. Abby wanted to talk with Jay before she left, but it didn't look like she'd get the chance.

But in the meantime, she was on her way to the Caribbean!

CHAPTER EIGHT

PRIVATE plane was the only way to travel, Abby decided. No, make that private plane and limousine.

From the moment Eugene had appeared at the door to her modest second-floor apartment, Abby felt as though she'd stepped into another world—because she had.

Parker was on the car phone as Abby climbed into the back seat of the car while Eugene stowed her one suitcase. Had she packed correctly? Who knew?

Abby had changed into the only tailored pantsuit she owned, desperately hoping it was appropriate for business travel.

Parker wore the same dark suit and white shirt as usual.

She sighed and settled back against the padded leather. Abby was becoming accustomed to the smooth ride of the plush car, so much so, that her own car now seemed cramped, noisy and bumpy. She'd never tire of riding in Parker's limousine. It was the ultimate way to travel.

At least that's what she thought until she flew in the plane.

Stepping on board, Abby noticed a dozen seats, then an open area with tables and conversation groupings. The whole inside was decorated like a contemporary living room or private club. All it lacked was a fireplace.

"I thought they only had planes like this in the movies!" she embarrassed herself by exclaiming.

"It comes in handy," Parker murmured, and stowed his briefcase in a side compartment. Then he smiled, but it was as though he'd mentally reminded himself to smile.

Something was obviously troubling him. Abby wanted to ask what, but didn't feel she had the right. Now if it had been Jay, she wouldn't have had to ask. Jay wasn't one to hide his feelings. But the brooding man who'd stopped to confer with the pilot definitely wasn't Jay.

Abby silently buckled herself into the cream-colored, extravagantly cushioned seat and waited for a chance to ask Parker what in the world her duties were going to be while they were on Colombé. Maybe if she was very lucky, some of those duties would involve lolling around on a beach while sipping tall drinks with tiny umbrellas.

As soon as Parker was seated across the aisle, he was back on the telephone. He hadn't given Abby any instructions, though she'd carried on a bag with various office supplies, her notebook and his schedule, just in case he wanted to work. She'd also slipped in a paperback novel, but decided it would appear more professional to wait before bringing the book out.

Abby could hardly believe she was traveling to an island—a *privately owned* island—with Parker Laird. Even though she'd dreamed of jetting off to exotic locales, the reality was making her apprehensive. She stole a look at him, hoping he'd remember that this was all new to her.

Parker closed his cellular phone and pressed the intercom button. "We're ready, Chris," he instructed the pilot.

"We'll take off as soon as we've got clearance from the tower," the pilot responded.

Parker leaned back and closed his eyes. He looked tired, Abby thought. His skin was paler than usual and dark marks were visible beneath his eyes.

And he was still as remotely handsome as ever.

Jay was good-looking, maybe at first glance even more superficially handsome, but Parker's features were defined and had more depth to them. Maturity, she thought. And maturity was attractive.

Thinking of Jay made her feel sorry that she hadn't had a chance to compliment him on his presentation. He was due to leave in a few days, but surely Abby and Parker would be back before he left.

"I apologize for springing this trip on you," Parker said, his eyes still closed.

Had he caught her studying him? "Valerie told me I'd have to be flexible."

Parker smiled, a genuine one this time. "You've had quite a week, haven't you?"

Laughing, Abby said, "It certainly beats typing production reports!"

He opened his eyes and, again, she noticed the intensity of his gaze. "Yes, I suppose it would. I hadn't realized you were dissatisfied in your job."

Oops. "I'm not dissatisfied." But did he really think she aspired to spend the rest of her days typing endless columns of numbers? "I just prefer some aspects of the job over others. Have you ever typed one of those reports?"

"No."

She knew he hadn't. "I realize it's got to be done, but it's sure tedious."

Parker nodded, thoughtfully, as though he'd never considered the typing of production reports before. He made a note—about what, Abby had no idea.

"We've been cleared for takeoff," announced the

pilot, and the plane began taxiing down the runway. Abby's heart picked up speed in time to the increasing beat of the engines. Her adventure was beginning.

When the plane leveled off, Parker unfastened his seat belt. "Did you get a chance to eat lunch?" He stood and removed his jacket, revealing his customary blinding white shirt.

Abby shook her head.

"Neither did I. Come on and I'll show you the galley."

Abby followed him to the back of the plane. Walking through so much space on an airplane felt strange to her.

Parker caught her looking around and gestured to the plush seating. "These all convert to beds. Watch." Deftly, he unfolded a small sofa and repositioned a table. Reaching toward the ceiling, he released the window curtains and showed her how they enclosed the bed for privacy.

"How clever," Abby marveled.

"I've logged a lot of hours here," he said.

Looking at the expression on his face, Abby privately thought he ought to log a few right now.

But Parker replaced everything the way it was. "The galley is back here. If the board members are flying, or I have guests, I usually arrange for an attendant, but since it's just us this trip, we're on our own."

Abby had wondered if flight attendant duties were part of an executive assistant's responsibilities. Well, if they were, he'd just have to tell her.

"There's the microwave and refrigerator." Parker pointed them out and showed Abby how everything worked and how to secure it when she was finished. "Let's see what we've got in here," he said, opening the refrigerator door. "What kind of food do you like, Abby?"

Abby found herself nearly faint with hunger. "A sandwich?"

Parker looked over at her, a half smile curving his lips. "Oh, I think we can do better than that."

He held her gaze for an extra second before turning back to the refrigerator. Abby's stomach felt as though the plane had taken a sharp dive.

There had been a lot of Jay in that look. But this was Parker. He hadn't meant anything.

Yes, that's what she should remember. This was Parker, her boss, not his brother, the flirt. As if Parker would ever flirt with her.

Parker, her boss, held two plastic-domed food containers and had obviously asked her a question. Guessing it had to do with whether or not she wanted whatever he was holding, she nodded.

He set the containers on the counter and withdrew two plastic-wrapped plates. "Veal medallions and potatoes or lasagna?" He read the labels on several more plates. "Chicken breast…unidentified beef." Parker read the one underneath and laughed. "Meatloaf and mashed potatoes! I asked Dimitri—he's the chef at the restaurant we use to cater the plane—if he knew how to make simple food and he apparently took me at my word." Chuckling, Parker poked a hole in the plastic cover and shoved the dinner into the microwave. "Have you decided what you want yet?"

A chef to cater the plane. There was so much she had to learn. But she did know one thing—meatloaf had no place in her fantasies. "I'll have the veal."

Parker withdrew it, then collected silverware. "If you'll carry the shrimp salads, we can set up in here."

Shrimp salad. Good grief. Abby followed him to one of the tables.

He flipped the top over to reveal a lipped surface and proceeded to set out the flatware.

Seeing him occupied with such a domestic chore gave Abby another jolt.

He glanced up at her. ''Didn't you think I knew how to set a table?'' he asked, as though he could read her mind.

''I never thought of you in that way.''

Parker took the salad plates and removed their domes. ''And what way is that?''

''A-a domestic, ordinary way, I guess.''

''Hmm. Mineral water? Coffee?'' He strode back to the galley.

''Mineral water is fine.''

Parker removed his entrée from the microwave and put hers in. ''So how do you think of me?'' he asked after handing her an opened bottle and glass.

Abby couldn't believe she was having this conversation while Parker was setting the table for their lunch. It was so unreal.

''I think of you as my boss.'' She eyed him warily as he folded a cloth napkin into thirds, made another fold, peeled down part and fanned it out, setting it next to her place with a flourish. ''Where did you learn to do that?''

Parker pulled out her chair and seated her. ''When I first started flying with my father, he'd hold meetings in here and I'd hang out with the chef. You think this is fancy, try flying with a chef.''

''Sounds good to me,'' Abby said.

Parker smiled. ''Eat your salad.''

''Yes, boss.'' She grinned back at him.

Parker gazed at her, then made a very unboss-like

comment. "I like it when you smile. People don't smile much when they're around me."

Abby wasn't smiling now. Her mouth gaped open like a fish.

Parker shifted. "What I mean is, I think the atmosphere at the office is so formal, people are inhibited."

"We don't smile much around Valerie, either," was all Abby could think of to say.

"I know. Neither do I," he confessed with a grin that was as winsome as any of Jay's.

Except Jay's easy charm didn't give her insides quite the same tug. Or maybe she was just hungry. Abby decided to concentrate on her salad.

"My father was a formal man and Valerie maintained that atmosphere when I took over," Parker continued. "I was young and I supposed the formality reassured people. And me." He stared down at his fork, then continued eating his salad.

Abby couldn't imagine Parker ever in need of reassurance.

As she ate, she considered what it must have been like for him to assume the responsibility of an international company while still in his twenties. He would have had to constantly prove himself to people who thought he was too young.

The circumstances would have been sobering for anyone.

During lunch, Parker talked about everything but business. He asked Abby about school, her family and what it was like growing up in a small town.

"I had a normal childhood," she told him.

"And what do you consider normal?" he asked.

"Oh, you know, going to school, playing with my friends, a mom who worked part-time so she could be home when my sisters and I got out of school. Girl Scouts, choir, piano lessons, hanging out at the mall, except it wasn't much of a mall, going out for pizza after football games…those sorts of things.'' She trailed off, conscious that she was babbling—conscious, too, that he was regarding her with an unsettling intentness. ''Isn't that what you did?''

''No,'' he said, after a pause.

''Well, what did you do?''

''I went to private school. After the instructional day, we had sports until five-thirty. Our driver picked me up and took me home for dinner and I did homework until bedtime. The next day, I did it all over again.'' He recited his childhood schedule without inflection.

''You had that much homework?'' She wrinkled her nose.

''It seems that way.''

''That's not normal.''

''It was normal to me.''

He'd probably been a straight-A student, too. ''I'll bet you wore uniforms. Navy-blue jackets and ties, right?''

Parker smiled—tightly, but it was a smile. ''How did you know?''

''Because you wear a dark suit all the time now.''

''I feel more comfortable in suits,'' he said with an appealing touch of defensiveness.

And he looked good in them. But he'd probably look good in anything.

Abby sat back. ''What about weekends and summers? Didn't you ever just hang out with your friends?''

''Until I was eleven, I went to camp in the summers. After that, I worked with my dad.''

"No friends?"

"I had friends." He reached for the empty salad plates and stood. "But I didn't have a lot of…hanging out time."

No wonder he was so wedded to his schedules. Abby followed him back to the galley. "You don't have free time now. I've never known anyone with a day as crammed as yours. You work in your car, you work in your plane. You even sleep in your office."

"That's a matter of efficiency and convenience." Parker checked the temperature on his meatloaf and put it back in the microwave for another minute. "If I need to talk with our overseas people, I sleep at the office rather than driving back and forth to home."

That made sense. "I hadn't thought about that."

The microwave buzzed and Parker removed his meatloaf.

Judging by the expression on his face, he was looking forward to eating it, and Abby wondered what it would be like to be so accustomed to fancy food that meatloaf would seem novel.

She couldn't wait to find out.

They landed on St. Thomas because the Laird jet was too large for the tiny airstrip on Colombé.

Abby pressed her face to the window as they taxied. "I thought islands were flat. This one looks like a mountain sticking up out of the ocean."

She wants to travel. I want to show her London, Paris and Rome. "You've never been to the Virgin Islands?" Parker asked, though he knew the answer.

"I've never been anywhere." As if suddenly aware of sounding too pathetic, she quickly added, "That's why I moved to the big city."

"Because you wanted to see the world?"

"Yes." She looked at him over her shoulder. "Does that sound silly?"

He shook his head. "No. It sounds admirable."

With a shy smile, she turned back to the window.

After diligently questioning her during the past several hours, Parker had compiled a mental dossier of Abby Monroe. She was a bright girl from a small town who'd had a conventional upbringing and now was ready for some excitement.

Jay had provided the excitement. It was as simple as that. Abby wasn't in love with him. What Jay had interpreted as attraction had only been her enthusiasm. She'd react that way with anyone—even Parker.

Fortunately, Abby Monroe was completely transparent, without a devious bone in her body. She had no hidden agenda. She wasn't trying to manipulate Jay; she wasn't out for what she could get. For that, Parker was very thankful.

Abby was a nice kid who craved a taste of the good life, and that was exactly what Parker intended to give her. A few days in the Caribbean—away from Jay—and she'd be thrilled. Jay would realize he hadn't been in love after all, head for El Bahar, and Parker would finally be able to shift some of the responsibility for Laird Drilling to his brother.

It was a good plan. No, a *great* plan. Everybody would win.

Parker gazed over at her, smiling to himself at the eager way she peered out the window. He checked his watch. "It'll be light for a couple more hours. Are you interested in seeing a bit of St. Thomas?"

"Oh, yes!" Abby breathed. "But isn't Mr. Ramsdell waiting for us?"

Oh, right. "I'll call him and let him know we'll be delayed."

"Will that be okay?" She bit her lip with an appealing touch of anxiety.

Something softened inside Parker.

The plane had taxied to a stop. "Life is casual on Kitt's island," he said. But because Abby probably wouldn't enjoy herself if she thought someone was being inconvenienced, he called the Ramsdell compound. "This is Parker Laird. My assistant and I have arrived in St. Thomas."

An lightly accented male voice spoke. "Welcome, Mr. Laird. All is ready for your arrival."

"Good. We'll leave on the tender in a couple of hours."

"Will you require any special preparations?"

Parker let a few seconds pass. "Not at the moment, thanks." He closed his telephone and smiled. "Ready to go exploring?"

Abby's face lit up with a smile so bright that Parker had no trouble understanding why Jay believed himself in love with her.

The cabin door opened and Abby squinted at the sunlight. "Oh, no! I forgot my sunglasses!"

"Not a problem." Parker urged her down the steps. "St. Thomas is known for its shopping. Remind me and we'll stop at a store before we leave for Colombé."

Parker rented a Jeep, tossed their luggage and his suit jacket in the back, and took off on the narrow mountainous roads of the island.

Abby gripped the open window and swiveled her head from side to side, exclaiming over everything from the mild weather, a relief from Houston's muggy heat, to the white-sanded beaches.

For his part, Parker nodded, and concentrated on

remembering that he was supposed to drive on the left side of the road.

He wished they had more time on the island. Abby would enjoy snorkeling at Coki beach. "Did you remember to pack your swimsuit?" he asked.

Abby's face clouded. "I didn't pack one."

"What?" Parker risked glancing away from the winding road. "You knew you were coming to the Caribbean and you didn't pack a swimsuit?"

"We're supposed to be working."

"Not twenty-four hours a day." Parker pulled off the road at a spot where there was a particularly good view of Charlotte Amalie.

"Oh, look!" Abby gazed into the harbor where the enormous cruise ships were docked, a look of intense longing on her face.

"Shall we get out so you can take a picture?" Parker asked.

Abby looked abashed. "I didn't bring a camera, either."

"Then we'll just have to fix that." Turning the car around, he headed toward the dock.

"Where are we going?" Abby asked as they wound down the hill.

"Shopping," Parker answered. "You need a swimsuit, a camera and sunglasses. How about a hat?"

Abby winced and Parker laughed.

"Don't worry about it. I rushed you and you're not used to packing quickly the way I am."

"Well, you need clothes, too!" she said.

"*I* didn't forget anything."

"But you don't have the right clothes." She sounded very certain.

"What's wrong with my clothes?"

"Look at the people." They'd entered a more populated area, and she gestured to the streets they passed. "No one else is wearing a suit, unless it's a swimsuit."

"I took off my jacket," he protested.

Abby rolled her eyes. "Do you see anybody wearing a tie?"

Parker didn't care if they were wearing ties or not. But Abby seemed to. Loosening the knot at his neck, he slipped off the tie.

"There. Doesn't that feel—Parker!"

Parker had tossed the tie over his shoulder. Since the Jeep he was driving didn't have a roof, the tie went sailing on the wind.

Abby turned all the way around in her seat. "Your tie is stuck on a bush."

Parker unbuttoned the top button of his shirt. "Better now?"

"But, your tie." She turned back around. "I can't believe you did that."

Parker had been trying for a devil-may-care gesture—something Jay might have done—but Abby's expression told him he hadn't made the impression he'd wanted. "I never liked that tie," he offered as an explanation.

But Abby was still looking skeptically at him, probably because his ties were all variations on a very narrow theme.

"It didn't hang right," he said, now wishing he'd kept the damn thing on.

"Oh." Her "oh" hung in the air between them.

Parker was going to have to work on his spontaneity. Surely it was a skill that could be learned like anything else.

Before the silence grew awkward, he arrived at the shopping area next to the dock and parked near a row of single-story buildings. ''We'll find the things you need here.''

Throngs of people wandered from shop to shop. ''What's going on?'' Abby asked.

''They're passengers from those two cruise ships,'' Parker pointed out. ''By the way, I'd like us to leave before the ships sail, so we need to be on the Colombé tender by seven o'clock.''

''That gives us less than an hour.'' Abby's forehead creased as she gazed down the rows of shops.

''Then let's get going.'' He took her hand and felt her tense. ''I move fast and I don't want to lose you in the crowd,'' he explained, hating the fact that he felt he had to keep doing so.

Abby laughed. ''Lead on.''

Parker laced her fingers through his, liking the feel of her hand. He felt an unexpected surge of protectiveness toward the flame-haired woman beside him, especially since Abby was gazing about her as though trying to see everything at once and not paying any attention to traffic. He enjoyed her unguarded enthusiasm and her obvious excitement at being here. ''I remember a diving shop nearby. You need a swimsuit, too, as I recall.''

''Only if you think we'll have time to swim.''

Parker looked down at her, grappling with a sudden vision of Abby, her legs revealed in a swimsuit. ''We'll make time.''

Parker Laird is holding my hand.

Desperately trying to act nonchalant, Abby looked everywhere but at him.

Why was she so *aware* of holding his hand?

Here she was on her first real trip anywhere and instead of looking and smelling and feeling the *dif-*

ferentness of it all, she could only obsess about Parker holding her hand.

Make that Parker pulling her hand. Within moments, he'd led her right across the street and into the mob of shoppers.

Abby held on as Parker cut right and left and doubled back through an alley between the rows of buildings. If she let go, she'd never find him again.

The thought made her grip his hand harder.

"You doing okay?" he asked, slowing marginally.

"If being turned around and completely lost counts as being okay, then I'm fine."

He laughed, something he'd been doing more often today. "If we get separated, head for the cruise ships. They're the tallest objects on St. Thomas."

Abby looked back over her shoulder at the ships. "Yeah, but they're leaving."

"You don't need to worry," he said, his voice quietly confident. "I'd find you."

And he would, Abby knew. He was that kind of man. He took his responsibilities very seriously.

But who takes care of him?

She was surprised at the thought, but even more when she realized the answer: Valerie. Valerie was more than an executive assistant; she was a surrogate mother.

And with Valerie and her Rolodex gone, there was no one to see to the extra details that allowed Parker to relax. He'd even had to make the arrangements for this trip when it should have been Abby's job.

She quickened her pace, though she was almost jogging as it was. Parker had been acting strangely all day and Abby decided it was because he was exhausted. She also decided that in Valerie's absence, it was her responsibility to get him to slow down and rest. *Someone* had to.

"Here it is," Parker announced. "Galiano's Dive Shop. There's a boutique next door."

They went inside, pushing past displays of post-cards, T-shirts, magnets and shot glasses.

Once she was past the tourist junk, Abby saw that the shop had a good selection of swimwear.

"Did *you* bring a swimsuit?" Abby asked Parker.

"Probably."

"That doesn't sound like a 'yes.'"

"If I didn't, I can borrow one from Kitt."

Abby pointed to a rack of men's suits. "You should buy one anyway."

"I—"

"No arguing."

A smile touched his lips. "Yes, ma'am."

It felt good to boss Parker around, especially since it was for his own good. "And while you're at it, make sure you've got casual clothes."

"You mean like this?" Parker held up a tie with neon bright seashells printed on it.

"I said casual, not tacky." Abby bypassed the skimpy two-piece suits, briefly wishing she had the sort of skin that tanned, and found the rack with mail-lots. "I'll just be a minute." Always assuming the swimsuit gods were with her. "The men's clothes are over there," she said pointedly.

Out of the corner of her eye, she watched Parker approach the shelves holding men's shorts and shirts. He took well to being bossed around, she thought with satisfaction.

Abby found several styles to try on, a couple with matching cover-ups. And, wonder of wonders, the dressing room had regular lighting and not the hideous fluorescent bulbs that made her skin look pale green.

Abby was a moderate height, but her legs looked longer and the suit she selected was cut high on the sides to emphasize what she considered to be her best asset. It came with a knee-length loose jacket. Just the short time she'd been on St. Thomas had convinced her to respect the bright sun of the Caribbean.

Abby had found a hat and was trying on sunglasses when a man approached her from behind.

"I'm going next door to buy snorkeling equipment. Have you been snorkeling before?"

She looked at the reflection in the mirror. "Parker?" Whirling around, Abby stared at him.

Parker had changed into white shorts and a knit top with St. Thomas and a colorful fish embroidered on the pocket.

He gestured to himself. "Good? Not good?"

"Good," Abby squeaked, then swallowed. No "relaxed fit" necessary for him.

"You sure?"

Oh, boy, was she sure. "You bought a suit, too, didn't you?"

Parker set a stack of clothes on the counter and held up a pair of black swim trunks bearing a sport company's logo. "How's this?"

Parker in swim trunks. "Fine," Abby managed, and set her own pile on the counter. She had to remind herself to breathe.

While she finished choosing sunglasses, Parker added a disposable camera and snorkeling gear to the pile. Within half an hour after entering the shop, they were back in the Jeep and headed along the dock. Now that was power shopping, Abby thought, and put on her new sunglasses.

Parker drove past the cruise ships to the smaller boats. ''There it is.'' He indicated a neat-looking yacht, rather than one of the large flat ferryboats that traveled between the islands. ''That's Kitt's private launch.''

A private launch. What else for a man who owned his own island? Abby marveled to herself as a man dressed all in white approached and unloaded their luggage.

Another man helped her out of the Jeep and across the short gangway, where a third man greeted her, and asked if she would like something to drink.

''I think I'm getting spoiled,'' she said to Parker. ''No,'' she corrected herself when a tall glass of iced tea appeared mere moments after she'd requested it. ''I'm *definitely* getting spoiled.''

Parker smiled down at her. ''You're easy to spoil.''

Meaning she was unworldly, Abby supposed. Well, so what? She *was* unworldly. It was nothing to be ashamed of. She eyed Parker as he exchanged a murmured conversation with yet another man, then joined her at the railing.

Parker Laird was as worldly as they came, but Abby didn't think he enjoyed himself very much. She hoped she was never too worldly to enjoy life.

''Do you want to go inside?'' He gestured to a door behind her.

''And miss the view? No way.'' She smoothed her hand along the brass railing, warm from the sun. ''You should stay here, too. It's good for your eyes.''

''Why?''

''Because you spend too much time focused on your computer screen or reading the drilling reports I type.'' She pointed to the horizon where the sun hung low in the sky, silhouetting islands in the distance. "Just look out there for a while. Let your eyes relax."

"Do my eyes look like they need relaxing?"

"Yes," Abby told him bluntly.

Parker looked at first surprised, then as if he were going to argue with her. He didn't, instead turning and obediently gazing at the horizon.

Sneaking a peek at him, Abby saw that he still held himself stiffly. "You can let the rest of you relax, too." She had to raise her voice to be heard over the engines.

"I am relaxed."

"That's not relaxed."

Just then, the yacht pulled away from the dock and Parker lurched sideways before grabbing the railing.

"See?"

He gazed at the islands without answering and Abby felt she'd overstepped the bounds.

"I'm sorry. I shouldn't—"

"No. Don't apologize. You're right." Parker turned to face her. "I don't relax often. I find it difficult to do nothing."

You also found it difficult making that admission, Abby thought.

He held her gaze a moment longer before staring out to sea again, the breeze ruffling his dark hair, which fell right back into place. Even his hair couldn't relax.

Abby sipped her drink. "Then don't think of relaxing as spending the time doing nothing. You're unwinding. That's doing something."

"Very creative. I'll give it a try." His mouth twisted in a wry smile and he hunched his shoulders in a way that told Abby they were probably in knots.

She longed to rub his shoulders the way she'd seen

her father rub her mother's after she'd spent long hours at her desk grading English papers.

The thought so unnerved Abby that she quickly gulped the rest of her drink and set the glass in one of the holders bolted to a deck chair. Her feelings for Parker were undergoing a dangerous and distressing change. Dangerous, because she shouldn't be having feelings for him at all, and distressing, because she couldn't seem to help herself.

"See those islands?" Parker pointed to gray-green smudges in the distance. "I've been trying to identify them and it's driving me nuts that I can't remember which ones they are." He turned away from the railing. "I'm going to check the map on the wall of the salon."

"Oh, no, you're not." Abby stepped between Parker and the doorway. "You aren't supposed to be thinking about identifying the islands. You're only supposed to look at them."

"I want to know what I'm seeing."

Abby gave him an exasperated look. "You're seeing the ocean and the waves and some islands thrown in to make the scenery interesting. You aren't supposed to work at it."

"But work is all I know!" He stared at her, lines of frustration creasing his forehead, then exhaling sharply, he closed his eyes. "This was a mistake. I should never have come here."

Abby was horrified. What had she been thinking? No matter what she felt, how could she have been so presumptuous as to imagine that she, lowly Abby Monroe, had the right to make personal judgments about Parker Laird? What business was it of hers how he lived his life or what he wore or whether or not he worked himself into an early grave?

Her cheeks burned so hot that her eyes started watering. ‘‘Mr. Laird…I must apologize—’’

‘‘*Mr. Laird*?’’ He’d opened his eyes and now saw her face. ‘‘Abby?’’

She couldn’t even look at him. ‘‘I’ve acted unprofessionally and I hope you accept my apology and attribute my impertinent behavior to inexperience and poor judgment.’’

He took her arm. ‘‘You sound like you’ve been spending too much time reading the dictionary. I have no idea what you think you need to apologize for.’’

She looked up at him. He appeared concerned, but not angry. ‘‘For ordering you around. I had no right.’’

‘‘You have as much right as anybody. Even more.’’

‘‘No.’’ She tried to shake her hand, but Parker had laid the back of his hand against her cheek.

‘‘I’ve upset you. Your face is hot.’’

And bright red, as well, she knew.

He squeezed her shoulders as the breath hissed between his teeth. ‘‘I’m angry with myself, not you. I *wanted* to take your suggestion about enjoying the scenery, but I couldn’t. *Couldn’t*.’’ His hands dropped. ‘‘I’ve forgotten how to relax, Abby. Do you think you can teach me how again?’’

She glanced up at him. Parker had accompanied his request with a winsome smile that made her lips curve in response.

He was either being incredibly decent or truthful, or both. Abby felt the heat seep away from her face and throat. ‘‘I’ll try, if we have time on this trip.’’

‘‘We’ve got time,’’ Parker told her. ‘‘I spoke with the captain and Kitt’s been delayed. We’ll be at loose ends on Colombé for a few days.’’

CHAPTER NINE

THE island of Colombé cast a magical spell over her. That could be the only explanation. Because after Abby absorbed the stunning, astonishing and utterly incredible fact that she was "at loose ends" on a Caribbean island with Parker Laird, and her only responsibility was to help him unwind, it was as though her Houston world ceased to exist. More than that, it was as though it had never existed—as if Abby had never been Parker's employee and as if Parker wasn't a powerful man with crushing responsibilities.

Colombé was a hilly island, like St. Thomas, and the Ramsdell compound was perched on the edge of a steep hill. As they approached through impossibly turquoise waters, the dying rays of the sun caught and gilded the bleached white stone of the house.

In Abby's mind, the house turned into a golden castle—and the dark-haired man at her side was the prince.

Warm breezes caressed her as she stepped off the boat, Parker's steadying arm beneath hers. The Ramsdell servants greeted them in a lilting island patois that only added to the otherworldliness.

Once again, their luggage was loaded into a Jeep for a drive up a winding road. Though it was twilight, Abby drew in her breath at the spectacular view of white beaches and a small town on the backside of the island.

But it was when they reached the white-walled Ramsdell compound that Abby knew she'd entered a land of enchantment. Palm trees lined the red-bricked drive and welcoming light spilled out from an arched entryway. In the distance, the ocean hummed a rhythmic background music.

The door opened as they approached, and they were greeted by a man dressed in the white everyone on the island seemed to favor. "Welcome, Mr. Laird. I am Aldo, the Ramsdell *major domo*. Please contact me should there be anything you require."

"Thank you, Aldo. This is my assistant, Ms. Monroe."

Aldo inclined his head. "If you will follow me, I will show you to your rooms."

Thank goodness. Abby couldn't wait to change out of her navy-blue pantsuit. Even though she'd shed her jacket, she felt drab and overdressed.

They followed Aldo down a long patio hallway around the edge of the house. At her first sight of the open-air arches, Abby stopped and stared. Tiled steps led through terraced gardens all the way to the beach.

Parker stopped next to her. "What are you thinking?" he asked after several moments of her openmouthed silence.

"I've never seen anything like it. I've never even *imagined* anything like it." She gazed up at Parker. "Why does Mr. Ramsdell ever leave here?"

With a gentle nudge in the small of her back, Parker urged her toward a patiently waiting Aldo. "Kitt leaves to make drilling pipe, which I'll buy, so he can afford the upkeep on this place."

"Do you have a home like this somewhere?" Abby asked.

"No."

"Would you like to have a place like this?"

"For just me?" He shook his head. "No."

"Then...why do you work so hard?"

Now Parker stopped to gaze out at the sea. The sun had set and the moon painted a gray stripe on the blue-black water.

He was silent for so long, Abby thought he wouldn't answer her question, and when he did, it wasn't the answer she'd assumed it would be.

"I work because it's expected of me. I need to keep the company strong and fiscally sound in order to present an attractive annual report to the board and stockholders." He ran his hand over the plaster arch before pushing away. "And to provide jobs for ambitious executive assistants," he added as they walked toward Aldo.

Abby smiled, though she privately wondered what Parker got out of driving himself as hard as he did. Money, sure, but when did the man have time to enjoy it?

Abby worked hard, but she had goals. She'd supposed Parker was working toward goals, too—if not an opulent getaway like this one, then for some other reason. He must want *something* to work as hard as he did.

Aldo was waiting for them near the end of the hallway. "These are the bedrooms." With a sweep of his hand, he indicated the doors that lined the wall. "Ms. Monroe, this will be your room. Mr. Laird, I've put you in the corner suite. Kenneth has seen to your luggage."

Aldo opened a door and Abby stepped inside, immediately delighted with the four-poster bed draped in gauze hangings. To the right was a bathroom in the same red tile as the hallway. "Oh, it's lovely! Imagine being able to walk outside the bedroom, across the hall, down the steps and wade right into the ocean!"

Parker watched her from the doorway. ''That sounds like a good idea. I'll join you.''

Abby hadn't actually been suggesting a walk on the beach, but the ocean *beckoned.* And Parker *beckoned.*

It was island magic.

''Shall I tell the chef to serve dinner in an hour?'' Aldo asked.

''That will be fine,'' Parker answered, still looking at Abby in a way that made her heart beat faster.

She quickly changed into a pair of shorts, bemoaning the fact that she hadn't brought anything long and filmy that would flutter in the ocean breezes. Not that she owned anything long and filmy, but since the whole house was like the set of a romantic movie, she felt she should dress the part.

When she opened the door, her leading man, illuminated by a silvery moon, was waiting for her under the arches. Barefoot, she crossed the hallway and Parker held out his hand. She grasped it and, together, they made their way down the sand-dusted steps to the beach.

It was a perfect setting for fantasies. In her heart, Abby knew Parker was only making sure that she didn't fall, but for the few minutes it took to navigate the steps, she pretended he was holding her hand because he wanted to keep her close.

''Careful, looks like sand has buried the last few steps.'' Parker swiped at the sand with his foot until the outline of the steps was visible.

Abby sighed. ''The beach is so beautiful—and the sand is white, not like the brown stuff in Galveston.'' She buried her toes in the warmth, then looked up at Parker shyly. ''I'm glad Mr. Ramsdell isn't here yet. Isn't that awful?''

"No." He laughed softly. "Because I feel the same way." His voice had taken on a husky quality.

"You do?" She'd thought he'd be angry about the delay.

Parker stepped closer. "Now I have a chance to spend some time alone with you."

Had he really said that? Or had Abby imagined it?

He gazed steadily at her, the moonlight making his eyes more silver than gray. "I don't often have the opportunity to go out with a woman without photographs appearing in the newspaper the next day. We don't have to worry about that here."

His voice struck a chord deep within her, bringing her secret fantasies about him to life. She'd never, *ever* thought he'd notice her and be attracted to her, but the look in his eyes was unmistakable.

And the response in her heart was undeniable.

"Oh, Parker." This had to be a dream, and Abby hoped she wouldn't wake up too soon.

Parker brought her hand to his lips and gently kissed her knuckles. She sighed softly.

"Let's walk," he said.

Abby melted into step beside him.

For once, Parker walked slowly. "I want to learn all about you."

Abby smiled at such a typical Parkerism—direct and to the point. "I think you learned all about me on the plane," she answered, remembering how she'd gone on and on about things that couldn't possibly have interested him.

"I learned about who you were. I want to know who you are and who you want to be."

"I think you know that, too. My goal is to become an executive assistant. That's why I was thrilled to fill in for Valerie."

"What about when you're not working? What do you do then?"

Abby laughed self-consciously. "I've been spending most of my time either working or studying."

He glanced down at her. "Be careful, or you'll end up like me."

"That wouldn't be bad. You're not at all like people think you are, you know."

A shadow crossed his face, but it was probably a trick of the moonlight. "Abby—yes, I am."

"Oh, no." She stopped walking and faced him. "They say you're a cold, unemotional perfectionist. Okay, you *are* a perfectionist, but you're not cold or unemotional, just reserved."

He looked as though he wanted to say something, then changed his mind. "Well, that's a relief." Bending down, he picked up a forked piece of white coral. "I thought people were saying much worse things about me."

"Oh, they do," Abby told him. "But they're wrong. They haven't seen the side of you that I have."

He threw the coral into the waves. "Abby—"

"They think you're a cold, ruthless businessman."

He drew a breath. "You should listen to them."

She shook her head. "You're a *good* businessman, and you're kind. But you're quietly kind, so people don't know about it."

He gazed unblinkingly at her, then stared out at the ocean. "I'm never kind unless there's a reason. Remember that."

The more Parker protested, the more Abby felt she had to convince him otherwise. "Stop thinking of yourself that way. Don't you think I know that once you found out Mr. Ramsdell had been delayed, you wanted to hop back on your plane and return to Houston? But you didn't because I was with you, and you knew I'd be disappointed, right?''

Parker stared at her. His lips were parted and he was breathing quickly, as though they'd been running instead of walking.

''Right?'' Abby prompted.

''Right.'' The word sounded as though it had scraped past his throat.

''And you made sure I had a swimsuit—and the blue dress and the gift certificates for Nancy and Barbara, and then there was the coffee—''

''Stop.'' He'd squeezed his eyes closed.

Did being caught in a kindness really bother him so much? Did he think his tough businessman reputation would suffer?

''It's okay,'' she said, daring to run her hand up and down his arm. ''I won't let anyone think you're going soft.''

Parker's mouth twisted. ''Abby—''

He gripped her shoulders and for a moment Abby thought he was going to shake her.

Then his expression changed. The lines across his forehead smoothed, his mouth relaxed and the grip on her shoulders became a caress.

''Abby.'' He sighed her name before drawing her close and capturing her lips.

He may have intended only a gentle embrace, but that wasn't what happened.

Whether it was the moonlight or the man or even the island magic, as soon as his lips touched hers, Abby surrendered.

She drew her arms around him and kissed him back, telling him without words that she'd seen past the hard, outer shell to the true person beneath.

Parker wrenched his mouth from hers. "I shouldn't—"

"Shh." Abby placed her fingers against his lips. "Yes, you most definitely should," she murmured, and drew his head to hers.

Parker kissed her then as though he'd been dying of thirst and she was a pool of cold, spring water.

How could he have fooled so many people for so long? Hadn't anyone bothered to get to know the man—this caring, passionate man?

He must have been desperately lonely, she thought, threading her fingers through his hair. Even his own family didn't understand him or appreciate him.

Only Abby had found the true Parker.

As Parker urged her lips apart with his breath-stealing kisses, Abby felt a deep sense of feminine satisfaction. She *knew* no other woman had unleashed this passionate side of Parker—not the true Parker. He wouldn't have dropped his guard with them the way he had with her.

He needed her.

With Abby, Parker wouldn't have to hide who he was. He could relax. She'd be a haven for him.

And just as she'd had to show him that he wasn't the ruthless person everyone said he was, she would have to show him that he needed her—that he could trust her.

That she loved him.

Abby didn't know whether the thought came from within her or was whispered on the Colombé breeze, but it didn't matter. It was true.

She was in love with Parker Laird.

It was all she could do to keep from telling him, especially when he freed her mouth to trail kisses against the side of her neck.

But Abby knew it wasn't time yet because the time to tell Parker that she loved him would be just after he admitted that he loved her.

He shouldn't have kissed her. He was supposed to be dazzling her, not kissing her, but when she looked up at him like he was a wounded bird she had to nurse back to health, Parker couldn't help himself.

Something had come over him once he started kissing Abby. It was as though he'd forgotten who and what he was, and had surrendered to his feelings. Parker wasn't used to having his feelings overrule his head. People who were ruled by their emotions got into trouble.

Jay was a perfect example, though he was a lot more sympathetic toward Jay now than he'd been this morning.

After Parker had said goodnight to Abby, he'd called his office to find that Jay had left seventeen messages for him. Parker guessed that there were an equal number of messages on Abby's machine. With any luck, after Jay had failed to find either of them he'd gone to whatever function was scheduled for this evening, and had already half forgotten a certain temporary executive assistant.

Now all Parker had to do was to see that a certain temporary executive assistant forgot all about Jay.

When Abby awoke the next morning, she was afraid that the hot Caribbean sun would burn away all last night's island magic.

She and Parker had kissed in the moonlight until the rising tide had lapped at their ankles, then they'd silently walked back to the house and eaten dinner.

Abby had been content in the silence, knowing that

Parker was thinking and that she needed to give him time to do so. He didn't have the advantage of a woman's intuition the way she did.

That same feminine intuition told her now that Parker might try to retreat behind his businessman's persona and Abby was determined not to let him.

She had dressed and was about to hunt for breakfast when a muted knock sounded at her door.

She opened it to find Parker. Abby searched his face, trying to read his mood from his expression.

"Are you ready for breakfast?" he asked.

"Yes. I was on my way to the dining room."

He smiled, a slow intimate smile, and Abby knew the island was still working its magic.

"Breakfast isn't being served in the dining room. Come and look."

Drawing her across the hallway, he pointed to the beach. At the foot of the steps, Abby saw Aldo standing next to a blue and white striped awning.

"Breakfast on the beach?" she asked with a delighted smile.

"I have fond memories of the beach," Parker murmured, and Abby sighed.

Once she was seated at the table under the awning, Parker dismissed Aldo and served her himself.

Abby ate mangoes and muffins, sausage and eggs, refusing hash browns until Parker insisted that she had never tasted such lightly crisped potatoes in her life.

He offered her a bite on a fork, his gaze on her mouth.

"You're right. They're wonderful," she admitted. "But if I eat too much, I won't feel like swimming and that water looks too good to resist."

"Which is why I thought we'd go snorkeling after breakfast," he said.

The entire time they ate, Abby found herself the object of Parker's complete attention. It was heady stuff, being the object of a powerful and attractive man's attention. But not once did Parker mention business or excuse himself to make telephone calls. It was as though his sole purpose in life was to be with her in this time and in this place.

And that was perfectly fine with Abby.

After breakfast, she changed into her swimsuit, slathered on sunscreen and met Parker at the beach.

He showed her how to inflate her vest and breathe through the snorkel.

"I feel like a giant duck in these fins." Laughing, Abby slapped her way to the edge of the water where an incoming wave caught the fins and tipped her over. Giggling, she looked to see how Parker fared, then caught her breath.

He'd stripped off his shirt before putting on the snorkeling vest and now Abby could see the muscles she'd felt last night when she'd kissed him.

He's gorgeous, she thought just before another wave slapped her. Salt water stung her nose and Abby ruefully vowed to pay more attention to what she was doing.

"Need help?" A few long-legged strides brought Parker next to her. Bending down, he lifted Abby to her feet.

"I'm having a little trouble negotiating the waves," she admitted.

With only a smile as her warning, Parker scooped her into his arms and waded into the ocean.

Abby took shameful advantage by looping her arms around his neck and nestling against his chest.

"Here you go." He set her down in waist-high water.

Abby thought he might kiss her then, but he put on his mask and gestured for her to follow him.

She was disappointed until she put her face in the water and saw the world beneath the surface.

Schools of tiny fish turned in silver waves at their approach. Larger fish allowed them to swim side by side. Rocks and coral jutted up from the bottom, making Abby glad she had on the hard rubber fins.

Abby didn't know which she enjoyed more, seeing the beautiful underwater world, or watching Parker's relaxed smile, but she'd treasure the memory of both for the rest of her life.

The rest of the day passed in a hazy dream. Parker had made arrangements for them to tour the coral gardens at nearby Buck Island in a miniature submarine. After that, they ate dinner and built a fire on the beach, talking long into the night.

Abby didn't ask when Kitt Ramsdell was due to arrive, because when he did, that would mean the end of her time alone with Parker.

And Abby was afraid that the Parker she'd come to love would disappear and she'd never be with him again.

''Would you like to visit the village today?'' Parker asked at breakfast.

''Can we?'' Abby had been certain that Parker would spend at least the morning working.

''If you want to.''

''I do...but when is Mr. Ramsdell coming?'' And she'd promised herself she wouldn't ask.

''Tomorrow or the next day. I don't know.'' Parker smiled and drank his orange juice.

''You don't know? I can't believe you're the same

man who schedules his days in fifteen-minute blocks.''

''Schedules aren't important here.'' And the look in his eyes told her what he *did* think was important.

Abby was almost afraid to breathe in case she broke the island's spell. The magic couldn't last forever, though she wished it would.

She and Parker explored the village's narrow cobbled streets and the pastel stuccoed buildings in the shopping area. They were seated at an outdoor café at noon when church bells began ringing.

The sound seemed to come from all around them and though she looked, Abby couldn't find the church.

''Up at the top of that hill,'' their waitress told them when Parker asked. ''The Church of Our Lady used to be a pirate lookout, but the French nuns who settled here took it over.''

After their lunch, they climbed the steep walkway leading to the small stone tower.

It was here, in the church courtyard on the edge of the cliff, that the peaceful timelessness of the island was the strongest.

She and Parker sat on a stone bench under a tree and gazed silently at the ocean and the other islands in the distance. Abby thought if she could freeze time in this instant, with Parker sitting beside her, she would. She didn't know any other way to keep the world from intruding. They couldn't stay here forever, and the knowledge made her sad.

Parker shifted and Abby closed her eyes, knowing before he spoke that their idyll was ending.

''It's time to leave. I know,'' she said, not wanting Parker to say it first.

''It doesn't have to be,'' he replied.

''Very gallant, but I know that you can't spend endless days here. Even if Mr. Ramsdell never comes, we have to leave tomorrow.''

''And how do you know that?''

''Because Jay's leaving on Tuesday. We're going back before he leaves, aren't we?'' She looked at him.

Parker's eyes darkened. ''And you want to say goodbye, to him, right?''

There was an edge to his voice that Abby didn't understand. ''Of course. Don't you?''

''We'll call him.''

''Parker!'' Abby was surprised into a laugh. ''You can't do that to Jay.''

He gave her a sharp look and stood, hands shoved into his pockets.

Abby stood, too, her legs sore from sitting so long. To get the kinks out, she started walking toward the church.

Parker followed her. ''You realize that once we leave, things will never be the same?''

''I know,'' Abby said, feeling a lump form in her throat. He was telling her that it would be business as usual once they left the island—that their island romance would remain just that.

She'd been foolish to dream otherwise. After all, he was Parker Laird and she was…she was nobody. Well, she wouldn't make a scene, she promised herself.

Tears smeared her vision and Abby stepped into the darkness of the church to hide them from Parker.

But the church wasn't dark inside. The entire stone wall behind the altar had crumbled away and had been replaced by glass which afforded a spectacular view.

She wiped her eyes as Parker reached her side.

''You're crying.''

''You weren't supposed to notice.''

With gentle fingers beneath her chin, Parker tilted her face to him. "But I did. Tell me why you're unhappy."

Couldn't he guess? "Because I don't want it to end."

His eyes warmed as they searched her face. "It doesn't have to end. Marry me, Abby."

She heard the words, but she didn't believe them. "What?"

"Marry me. Here. Now. Before the world intrudes."

"*Marry* you?"

"Yes." Parker kissed her quickly. "I don't want to go back to being the person I was. That person lived in a black-and-white world. With you, I see things, taste things and feel things as I never have before. I need you, Abby. I need you to put color into my world."

He needed her. He wanted to *marry* her. Abby was so full of emotion, she couldn't speak.

"You feel the same way, don't you, Abby? Tell me you feel the same way," he demanded.

"Oh, Parker!" Her breath caught on a sob.

He folded her into his arms, murmuring her name. "Abby, my Abby. Marry me. Now."

"Now?"

"Now." He turned her to face the view of the ocean. "It's perfect here. Perfect now. We could wait and plan to come back, but it wouldn't be the same. You *know* it wouldn't be the same."

"I know," she breathed. "But my family..."

"I understand that it's asking a lot. My family won't be here, either." He kissed her temple. "But I don't want to share this moment with anyone. I want to keep it for us. If we're married now, then we'll always have this. No matter what happens, we'll have this place in our hearts.''

Abby didn't think there was room in her heart for any more. ''But, Parker, I—I can't get married wearing shorts!''

''Then we'll buy you a dress—'' he kissed her ''—and flowers—'' he kissed her again ''—and a ring.''

A ring. It was really going to happen. She was going to marry Parker Laird. Now. Her parents would understand. She knew they would.

In a daze, Abby followed Parker as he found the priest, made arrangements to return at sunset and learned how to take care of the legal formalities, which merely consisted of the priest telephoning the local magistrate.

Then they returned to the village and Parker left her at a tiny dress shop.

Abby found two white dresses, but neither seemed right. In fact nothing seemed right, except a certain icy blue dress with matching sandals that she'd tucked into her suitcase just in case. She never dreamed that the ''just in case'' would be her wedding.

The shop's owner let her use the telephone and Aldo agreed to bring the dress. Abby found a delicate lace mantilla to drape over her head and shoulders, and a filmy white peignoir for her wedding night.

Her wedding night.

Tonight.

She shivered, both cold and hot at the same time. Was marrying Parker what she wanted? She thought of the man who'd shared the past two days with her and knew her feelings wouldn't change with time. This was what she wanted.

By the time she'd completed her purchases, Aldo had arrived with the dress.

Abby changed and with the shop owner's help, fashioned the mantilla over her hair. A darkly handsome Parker arrived as they were pinning it into place.

"You look beautiful," he told her, and helped her into the Jeep.

Handing her an enormous bouquet of white hibiscus, roses and baby's breath, he asked, "You haven't changed your mind, have you?"

"Oh, no." And Abby knew she wouldn't. Nothing she'd ever done felt as right as marrying Parker. It was unexpected, and it was fast, but in her heart, she knew it was right.

And so at sunset, in front of a priest in a stone church, high above the ocean, Abby pledged her heart to Parker Laird.

Aldo was waiting for them when they returned to the Ramsdell compound. "Congratulations, Mr. Laird." He inclined his head to Abby and took the box containing her peignoir. "Mrs. Laird."

Mrs. Laird. Abby stared at the simple gold band on her finger. She was Mrs. Parker Laird.

"I took the liberty of moving Mrs. Laird's things to your suite and the chef has prepared a wedding supper for you. Again, on behalf of the staff, I extend our very best wishes."

Parker murmured something appropriate and then he and Abby were alone.

She stared at her ring.

"Having second thoughts?" he asked lightly.

"No, it's just..." She looked up at him. "What are people going to say?"

"Congratulations, I hope," he answered smoothly.

With his hand in the small of her back, he urged her down the oceanside hallway to his suite.

"You know what I mean," Abby said.

Outside his door, Parker stopped and put a finger to her lips. "You are not to think about that tonight. As your new husband, I order you to obey."

Abby grinned. "I promised to love, honor and *cherish*. There was no 'obey.' I made certain of that."

"Then I insist you honor my request."

"Okay."

They both laughed and it broke the tension that Abby had felt since Aldo had left them.

The door to Parker's suite was open and Abby caught the flicker of candlelight on a table set for two. She started to enter the room, but Parker stopped her by sweeping her into his arms and carrying her over the threshold.

"Good grief. This room is as big as my whole apartment is in Houston." Her *former* apartment. "Parker! I don't even know where I'm going to live."

"Not tonight." He set her down. "Tonight is for us." He kissed her, gently at first, then with increasing passion.

By the time he broke the kiss, Abby had forgotten that there even was a Houston.

"I see Kitt's very efficient staff has chilled champagne for us." Parker reached for the bottle and peeled away the foil.

While he opened the champagne, Abby noticed that Aldo had laid out her nightgown on the bed in a swirl of white chiffon. Against the navy satin comforter, it looked like the whitecap of an ocean wave.

Something about that swirl of white brought home to Abby the enormity of her changed status. A week ago, Parker Laird barely knew her name. Now, she was his wife.

Wife. She was a wife. Parker Laird's wife.

Abby swallowed, barely aware of the muted pop of the champagne cork and the fizzing sound as Parker filled two flutes.

All she could do was stare at the nightgown on his bed.

"Abby?" Parker handed her a glass of champagne.

She turned to him, tried to smile, and couldn't.

"In the absence of a best man, I'd like to propose the wedding toast." Parker raised his glass. "To us. May we always be able to keep the world at bay."

Abby sipped her champagne, conscious that Parker watched her over the rim of his glass.

She should probably say something or make a toast, as well, but her mind was blank. Her hand trembled, so she set the champagne flute next to one of the place settings and laced her fingers together.

In the silver dome covering the plate, she saw her reflection and that of the dark-haired man beside her.

"Abby?"

"S-should I change?" Her tongue stuck to the roof of her mouth.

Parker studied her, then set his glass down and took both her hands in his. Her heart picked up speed.

"Abby, you're a beautiful, desirable woman and I want to make love to you very much. But I also realize that events have moved very quickly and I don't want you to do anything that makes you uncomfortable." He leaned down and placed a kiss on her shoulder.

Make *love*. Abby closed her eyes and felt him kiss her again.

She tilted her head back and Parker kissed the side

of her neck, his breath sending shivers down her spine. Her heartbeats changed to slow, molten thuds.

"Abby?" he whispered near her ear.

"M-maybe I should change now."

"Does this mean you want to make love tonight?"

"Oh, yes, please." She leaned forward and raised her mouth for his kiss.

He chuckled softly against her mouth, his fingers at the back of her neck. As he slid open the zipper of her dress, he said, "Then you won't need to change into your nightgown until the morning."

Something raced up her spine. Abby didn't know whether it was the breeze from the open windows, excitement, or just plain nerves. She shivered.

"Dare I hope that you're trembling with desire?" Parker breathed against her skin, raising gooseflesh.

"O-oh, yes..."

"Liar." He chuckled. "But a charming one."

He was thinking she was unsophisticated, Abby knew. She *was* unsophisticated. He was probably regretting their hasty marriage already.

She gasped as her dress slithered down her arms. Parker eased it over her hips, his hands warm against her waist, until the dress puddled at her feet in a pool of sparkles.

Abby was in her underwear in front of Parker Laird. *He's my husband*, she told herself, but he still felt like her boss.

"You're beautiful," he whispered, his gaze sweeping over her. "And you've got great legs. Did you know I had a thing for your legs?"

"Y-you did?"

"I do." A half smile tugged at the corner of his mouth. Parker bent down and plucked her dress from the floor, draping it carefully over a chair. ''I don't want anything to happen to your wedding dress.''

It was this small gesture revealing his sentimentality that banished Abby's nervousness. Parker had been as moved by their wedding as she'd been. The cold knot in her stomach dissolved into something warm and liquid.

''Would you like to put on your robe and eat the supper Aldo prepared for us?'' Anticipating her response, Parker had lifted one of the domed covers.

''No.''

His head snapped toward her. ''No?''

Abby stepped toward him. ''Not yet.''

The desire she saw in his eyes gave her a new feminine courage. The desire she felt within herself gave her daring.

Holding his gaze with her own, Abby unhooked her bra, shimmied it off her shoulders and let it fall to the floor.

Parker dropped the silver dome, the clank loud in the breathless silence of the room.

She smiled. His lips parted.

Abby kicked off her sandals.

Parker swallowed. She could hear him breathing—quick shallow breaths that told her he wasn't as calm as he pretended to be.

Slowly, savoring this heady new power, Abby walked toward him. ''You, my dear husband, are overdressed.''

She'd never seen a man remove a suit jacket as fast as Parker did. Reaching for his tie, she flung it in a gesture reminiscent of the way he'd discarded his tie on St. Thomas.

Parker stared at her with such intensity that Abby nearly felt his gaze touching her.

It wasn't enough. She wanted him to actually touch her—and she wanted to touch him. She raised her hand.

"Once you touch me...once I touch you—" He broke off, his voice sounding like raw silk. "Abby, I don't want to hurt—"

She pressed her fingers to his lips and felt him shudder. Bringing her other hand to his face, she cupped his cheek. "I love you."

"*Abby.*"

It was as though she'd released a torrent of passion that Parker had dammed for a lifetime.

Murmuring incoherently, he rained kisses on her face, her shoulders and her breasts, at which point, Abby's knees buckled.

Parker lifted her in his arms and strode to the huge bed, reverently settling her in the cool satin depths. Her negligee slid to the floor.

The guttering candles illuminated the fierce desire on Parker's face as he stripped off his clothes before gathering her in his arms. "Abby, my sweet Abby," he murmured, his voice rough with need.

His hands worked their magic, building in her a desire for closeness that couldn't be satisfied by anything other than the ultimate act.

And when Parker at last joined with her, Abby knew it was more than a mere physical union, it was the bonding of their hearts and souls.

CHAPTER TEN

ABBY sat on the edge of the bed and held up the white negligee. "I don't know why I wasted my money on this since I haven't had a chance to wear it yet," she complained.

Her new husband propped himself on an elbow. "You could put it on now."

"You'd just take it off again."

Parker reached across the bed, grabbed her by the waist and slid her next to him. "You're right." He kissed her between the shoulder blades, and Abby sighed.

"Parker, we've got to get up. It's lunchtime and we missed breakfast."

"I had you for breakfast."

Abby laughed. "Parker, I'm hungry—for food!"

"I suppose you're right," he said, releasing her. "The staff probably has a pool going on when we surface."

Abby gasped and he laughed.

"You're such fun to tease."

Abby was a bit embarrassed by her newly married status and the fact that it was noon and they were still in bed.

Parker reached for the phone. "I'll call Aldo and have him bring lunch."

"Here?" Abby squealed and clutched the sheet to her chest.

"Why not here?"

"Because..." She gestured at herself, then Parker, then at the bed.

"Your point?" Parker gave her an innocent look.

Abby wasn't giving in. "Because!"

He shook his head in mock disappointment. "All right. We'll get dressed." With a complete lack of self-consciousness, he got out of bed and crossed the room.

Abby sighed, still unable to believe she was married to him. Still unable to believe that she could experience such happiness without bursting.

"Hey," he called from inside the bathroom. "This tub is big enough for two." A second later, he appeared in the doorway and crooked his finger.

It was two-thirty before Abby got her lunch. She could barely look Aldo in the face, a fact which caused Parker no end of amusement.

They were lazing on the beach when the sound of raised male voices drifted down to them. At first, Abby thought the staff was arguing, but the voices got louder.

"Where are they?"

"Mr. Laird!" Aldo's usually unflappable voice was definitely flapped.

Parker and Abby looked at each other, then Parker stepped from under the awning.

"Parker! Where's Abby? What have you done with her?"

"Jay? Parker, is that Jay?" Abby scrambled off her lounge chair, smiling at the sight of Jay, dressed all in beige and cream linen. Then she looked up at Parker and her smile faded.

He was obviously not pleased to see his brother.

"Abby!" Jay had seen her and galloped down the rest of the steps. "Oh, Abby, how I've missed you!"

He grabbed her in a giant bear hug, nearly knocking her off balance.

"Jay!" Her hat and sunglasses fell to the sand and she clutched at him, just to keep from following them.

"Are you all right?" he asked, releasing her.

"Of course, I'm all right." She laughed. Jay was being his usual dramatic self. "More than all right."

"What are you doing here, Jay?" Parker snapped.

"Parker!" What was the matter with him?

"I might ask you the same question." Jay glared at him. "Why didn't you return my calls?"

"I didn't return anyone's calls."

"So I heard."

Abby looked from brother to brother, trying to figure out the source of Parker's antagonism. "Mr. Ramsdell was delayed, so we waited for him," she offered.

"Delayed?" Jay raised his eyebrows. "You tore out of the office on *Friday* and you've been twiddling your thumbs since then? I didn't even get a chance to talk to Abby, here."

She'd felt guilty about not being able to tell him what a great job he'd done on his presentation. "We would have come back before you left, Jay," she said.

Parker said nothing at all. He was transforming into the unemotional businessman right before her eyes.

"Would you? How about it, Parker? Would you have brought her back before I left?"

"Yes."

"Well, I don't believe you." Jay touched a finger to his lips. "You see, when you and Abby didn't come back that night, I discovered you'd left town. Here I thought you were off to a meeting someplace in Houston, but no. You *left the country*." Jay shoved his hands into his pants' pockets. "But I didn't find that out until I tracked down Kitt Ramsdell. He says you already have his pipe bid, by the way.''

Parker glanced at her and Abby realized that Jay had said something significant. She didn't understand quite what, though. She wished Parker would say something. The way he just stood there was making her nervous.

''Oh, and don't worry. He didn't tell me where you were. I figured that out all by myself.''

''Jay, you act like we were hiding from you,'' Abby said, expecting Parker to agree with her.

''Because you were,'' Jay said.

Abby found herself getting irritated by him. If he'd be quiet for just a few minutes, Parker could straighten out this misunderstanding.

''Even I'm entitled to a few days' rest,'' Parker said.

''Don't give me that. You wanted to keep me away from Abby and you know it!''

''Jay!'' Why was he saying such things?

He grabbed her hand. ''Abby, I've got to talk with you. I wanted to talk with you before the board meeting, but Parker convinced me to wait until afterwards. Only afterwards, you disappeared.'' He sent a scorching look toward his brother.

''Jay, don't.'' Parker approached and put his arm around Abby's shoulders. ''You'll find that things have changed.''

''Why?'' Jay's eyes widened and he looked back and forth from Parker to her. ''What have you done to her?''

''Jay, I'm fine.'' Abby looked up at her husband, waiting for him to tell his brother they were married.

''Abby is my wife.''

Abby wiggled the fingers of the hand Jay held.

He stared down at the ring, then dropped her hand as though it burned him. "You *married* her?"

Jay staggered back. Abby expected him to be surprised, but his expression was outraged.

Then, with an inarticulate howl, Jay lunged at Parker. Abby leaped aside.

"You married Abby!" His mouth twisting, Jay swung at Parker.

Parker avoided the punch, which infuriated Jay even more. "How could you do that to her?" This time his fist connected with Parker's jaw in a sickening crunch.

Abby screamed.

Parker took the punch without defending himself. "That's enough, Jay." He touched the corner of his mouth with the back of his hand.

"Enough? I'll show you enough." Arms flailing, Jay barreled into Parker, knocking them both to the sand.

"Jay! Stop!" Abby tried to drag him off Parker without success.

Finally, Parker captured both Jay's arms and rolled him over, pinning him in the sand. "Stop it!"

Breathing heavily, Jay spit sand out of his mouth.

Abby was so shocked she couldn't speak, but not so shocked that she wasn't hurt by Jay's reaction. Was this the way everyone would react to their marriage? Outrage?

"You're upsetting Abby," Parker said quietly, still holding his brother down.

"Oh, that's rich!" He struggled briefly, then stopped and glared.

"If you think you can control yourself, I'll let you up."

Jay said nothing, but Parker rocked back and stood.

Picking himself up, Jay fastidiously brushed sand from his linen jacket and pants.

Abby and Parker watched him.

When he finished, Jay stared back at them. ''Well, surely you aren't expecting my congratulations.''

Tears stung Abby's eyes.

''You'll do anything for the business, won't you, Parker? And you don't give a damn who gets hurt.''

Parker's eyes flicked toward Abby, then back to Jay. ''Don't.''

Jay shook sand out of his hair. ''So when did you two get married?''

''Yesterday at sunset,'' Abby whispered.

Jay's eyes turned to her. ''Just in time for a wedding night—eh, Parker?''

Under Jay's scrutiny, Abby felt herself blush.

Raising his fist, Jay took a step toward Parker. ''You—''

''Stop it! Why are you being so horrible? Can't you just be happy for me?'' Abby pleaded.

''Happy? Oh, Abby.'' Jay dropped his arm, his shoulders slumped. He looked at Parker, pain distorting his face. ''She was sweet and fresh and innocent and you spoiled it all in the name of business!''

''Abby, go on up to the house,'' Parker said.

''No, Abby. Stay, if you want to hear how he married you to keep you away from me.''

''Don't be ridiculous, Jay.'' Abby's laugh fell flat.

''You don't believe me?'' Jay gestured to the silent Parker. ''Ask him. Go ahead. Ask him why you suddenly had to fly to a remote Caribbean island and stay here without your host.''

''Mr. Ramsdell...was delayed.''

''He was never coming. Was he, Parker?''

Abby felt chilled. Parker's eyes were a stormy gray,

his face cold and hard. Nothing remained of the man who had spent the last two days with her—the man she'd married.

Jay approached her, his voice now gentle. ''Abby, I went to see Parker Friday morning to tell him how I feel about you.'' Jay took her hand, but she snatched it away. ''To tell him that I needed time to be with you. We had something special and I couldn't take off for El Bahar and leave you.''

''No,'' she whispered.

''I was going to tell the board, but he convinced me to wait. That was all the time he needed to get you out of there. I guess he figured out of sight, out of mind, right Parker?''

Deny it. Abby didn't want to believe Jay, but Parker wasn't saying anything. Why wasn't he saying anything?

Though she didn't want to, Abby began to replay the events since Friday against what Jay had just told her.

She *had* thought it strange that they'd had to leave so quickly. And the way Parker ushered Jay out of her office...

''You aren't in love with Abby and she isn't in love with you,'' Parker said.

''And you are?''

''Abby and I are married,'' he stated flatly.

''So now I'm supposed to fly off to El Bahar like a good boy and all will be fine? Think again, brother.''

''Jay, don't screw up this opportunity because you want to get back at me. When you calm down, you'll see that I've done you a favor.''

A favor? Abby felt like she'd been slapped. Parker was still talking, but she'd stopped listening.

He married you to keep you away from me. Parker had stood by while Jay accused him of ridiculous things, but now that Jay threaten the El Bahar project, Parker couldn't stop talking and the ridiculous accusations didn't seem so ridiculous anymore.

Nothing Jay said would have convinced her he was telling the truth like seeing Parker leap to defend his company.

I'm never kind unless there's a reason. Remember that.

And she'd forgotten.

"You thought if Abby wasn't available, I wouldn't have any choice but to go to El Bahar," Jay was saying.

"If you don't take this job, you'll never work at Laird again!"

"News flash. I don't want to work at Laird. I'm going to start my own company in direct competition with you, big brother. And when I tell your customers what you did, they'll be lining up to do business with me."

Abby couldn't stay quiet any longer. "You married me so Jay would go to El Bahar?"

"The light dawns," Jay mocked. "Hope you signed a great pre-nup, honey."

"What're you talking about?" Abby asked.

"A prenuptial agreement," Parker answered. "And no, she didn't."

Jay whistled. "You're slipping, Parker. Abby, good news. You ought to get at least a couple of million in the divorce settlement. And if you want, I'll help you really skewer him."

Abby burst into tears.

"See what you've done?" Parker shouted.

"What *I've* done? You seduced her—"

"*Stop it*!" Abby screamed, and covered her ears. "Stop it, both of you!"

The two men stared at her.

She lowered her hands. "Is what Jay says true? Did you bring me here to keep me away from him?"

For an instant, Parker's expression changed and Abby saw through the tough-businessman exterior to the man beneath, then a bleakness settled over his features. "Yes."

With that one word, he broke her heart and Abby was freed from the island magic.

Only it hadn't been magic. It had been nothing more than stupidity. What had Jay called her? Innocent and fresh? He'd left off stupid and gullible.

Abby was breathing hard, but she felt like she wasn't getting any oxygen. She swallowed, her mouth dry and gritty.

Everything Parker had told her had been a lie. A lie calculated to fool a naive girl who had inadvertently gotten in the way of a business deal.

But yesterday…the church…their wedding.

Last night. *Last night.*

Lies. All lies.

"No!" Abby's knees gave way and she collapsed on the sand, sobbing from the depths of her being.

"Abby, Abby."

But the arms that closed around her were Jay's and she sobbed harder.

"Shh. We'll make him pay for what he did to you."

"I—thought—he—loved—me!" she hiccuped. How could they share such a profound intimacy without love?

But Parker had never said he loved her, had he?

And he wasn't saying so now.

Abby clutched at Jay's shirt and cried, not even attempting to save her pride.

"You know," Jay said, "they always said Dad had no heart, but I thought there was a chance for you—until now."

"Abby—"

"Stay away from her." Jay's arms closed tighter around her.

"I will," she heard Parker say. "You don't have to leave the company. In fact, you can have it. I'll go to El Bahar in your place."

"What?"

Abby stopped crying.

Parker's face was pale. "You've wanted a chance to prove yourself. This is it. As of right now, you're in charge."

Parker looked down at Abby, his eyes as dark as she'd ever seen them. "I never meant to hurt you, Abby. I'll instruct the lawyers to see to our divorce at once. They'll keep it quiet and no one ever has to know we were married."

"And you think that makes everything all right?" she cried.

"No, but it's the best I can do. In the meantime, you'll have Jay to console you."

And without looking back once, Parker turned and climbed the steps to the house.

El Bahar—eight months later.

Parker hadn't bathed in a week, but neither had any of the other men at the drilling site. Water was being trucked in for cooking and drinking purposes only.

Parker had stayed at the site for three crew rotations, but now he was headed back to the main camp.

''Yer back, and I'm stayin' downwind of ye.'' Ian Douglass greeted him as he climbed out of the transport truck.

''Any luck on finding the water leak?'' Parker asked.

''No, and if we don't find it soon, you'll have to double your hazard pay to get a crew to agree to go out there.''

''Then we'll double it,'' Parker stated.

''Parker, lad, what's yer hurry? Yer already months ahead of schedule.''

Parker wanted the income from the wells coming in as soon as possible. Although he swore to anyone foolish enough to ask that he wasn't concerned about leaving his brother in charge of Laird Drilling, he knew Jay was in over his head.

But by how much, he deliberately ignored. Since the day he'd flown to El Bahar, Parker had not read a report or listened to a news broadcast. He'd worked and worked hard. He set a grueling pace and generously paid the workers who were willing to keep up.

All business mail was screened by Ian, who had strict instructions to share only cataclysmic news—such as Jay filing for bankruptcy.

That left personal mail.

With each batch, Parker braced himself for a heavy cream envelope announcing Abby's marriage to Jay, since the divorce was long since final. Or at least a note from his mother with news of an engagement.

After months passed with no announcement, Parker had taken to reading the society section of the Houston newspaper he had sent over.

There was only an occasional mention of Jay's attendance at some sedate function or another—the kind he usually avoided.

From Abby, there was nothing. His lawyers had informed him that she'd signed the divorce papers and refused the settlement he'd offered. He'd put it in an account in her name anyway.

Parker had avoided thinking about their time on Colombé—or the shattered look on her face when he'd left.

He had no explanation for his actions, either to himself or to others. Somehow, he'd become caught up in his own seduction. He'd gone too far and had actually convinced himself that he was marrying Abby as much for himself as he was to protect the company.

On his way to his quarters, Parker stopped by the trailer that acted as the main office. His mail had been collected in a plastic bin with his name on it.

He checked for an announcement or a letter, found one from his mother, ripped it open and scanned the contents. No mention of anything except how wonderfully Jay was doing.

His mother always thought Jay was doing "wonderfully", so that didn't mean anything.

There was no mention of Abby.

Parker gathered the weekend editions of the newspapers and headed for the showers.

Standing under the hot spray, he acknowledged that he was bone-deep tired. Maybe he'd read the newspapers and take a nap.

He always waited until he was exhausted to sleep, because he didn't want to dream. The first few nights in El Bahar, dreams of Abby and Jay had haunted him. Now, for some reason, he found himself thinking about Abby again.

After his shower, Parker stretched his sore muscles on the bed and tortured himself by picking through the society columns.

The very first paper he opened contained a picture of Jay laughing at a table with a woman.

And the woman wasn't Abby.

Romance Redux? asked the headline.

"Houston bachelor Jay Laird has been spotted around town with former flame Lisa MacKenzie...."

Parker stared at the photograph. Jay was back with Lisa? He checked the date on the paper and found three more recent editions, which he immediately tore open. In one, there was another picture of Jay and Lisa.

So just how long had Jay's great love for Abby lasted?

A sudden rage bubbled inside Parker.

How *dare* Jay treat her that way? He'd sworn it was different with Abby and after the scene on the beach, Parker had believed him. No one who had seen his brother's fiercely protective expression as he held the sobbing woman in his arms could doubt the depth of Jay's feelings. And the way Abby had clung to him...

Jay had probably run the company into the ground, too.

"Ian!" Parker bellowed. He shoved his feet into sandals and went tearing across the compound to the office trailer.

"Ian!"

Crewmen stopped and stared. Parker ignored them.

Ian appeared in the office doorway. "What's happened?"

Parker pushed his way inside, slamming the door

with such force that the trailer shook. "How fast can we pump oil?"

Ian rubbed the back of his head and sucked air between his teeth. "At the rate you're going, I'd say 'bout three months, give or take a couple of weeks."

"We'll be online in a month."

"A month? Are you daft, lad? You won't get one drop out of that pipe before April, unless you work like one possessed."

Three and a half weeks later, Parker was on a plane to Houston.

No one knew he was coming. He didn't want anyone to have a chance to hide any disasters.

Parker Laird was back, and he was taking control once more.

After going through customs in Houston, Parker hired a car and drove straight to the Laird building where he discovered somebody's junker of a car occupying his parking spot.

Inexplicably, this angered him and he stormed inside the building and marched up to the receptionist. In his hand, he gripped the newspapers with Jay's photos. "Where has my brother parked his lazy carcass?"

"Mr. Laird!"

"Well? Where is he? Or maybe I shouldn't assume that he shows up for work every day."

"Oh, yes. H-he's in your old office, sir."

Parker lowered his voice. "My *old* office?"

The woman nodded and reached for her switchboard. "Shall I—"

"Don't you dare warn him that I'm coming." Crossing to the elevators, Parker punched the button, all the while staring at the receptionist, whose hand was still poised over her switchboard.

It would be interesting to find out whether she warned Jay or not.

At least the building was still standing and judging from the full parking garage, Jay hadn't had to lay off many employees.

Parker erupted from the elevator and automatically glanced toward Abby's desk.

A young, dark-haired woman he'd never seen before sat there now. "Excuse me, you can't—"

"Yes, I can," he snarled, cut through the conference room and burst into his office.

"Parker!" Jay and Valerie exclaimed in unison.

Parker searched the room, which looked pretty much the way he'd left it.

Jay stood. "Why didn't you tell me you were coming?"

"I wanted to *surprise* you."

Valerie bustled over and took his coat. "Could I get you some coffee?"

"No. Thanks," he added belatedly.

She glanced at the two brothers, then gathered the scheduling book and left, discreetly closing the door behind her.

"Have a seat." Jay gestured to the chair by the desk and sat in the seat behind it.

The power seat, Parker noted. So that was the way he was going to play it.

"Hey, congratulations," Jay said. "I got word that the first barrel of oil made it through the pipeline. Didn't take as long as we expected, did it?"

"Only because I was efficient and worked hard."

"Good job." Jay sat back, smiling complacently.

They regarded one another, then Parker slammed the newspapers on his desk. "Why the *hell* aren't you married?"

Jay blinked. ''Lisa and I just got engaged. We haven't set a date yet.''

''*Lisa*? What about Abby?''

''What about her?''

The more composed Jay stayed, the angrier Parker got. ''I thought she was the love of your life.''

''I'm very fond of her.''

''Then why didn't you marry her?''

Jay's eyes narrowed. ''Well, there was a little problem.''

Parker couldn't remain in the chair. He stood. ''If you've hurt her—''

''You mean like you did?'' Jay wore an expression that Parker had never seen on his face before. It was a cold watchful expression that reminded him of their father when he was blazingly angry.

Parker tempered his words. ''Where is she?''

''She doesn't work in this department any longer.'' Jay picked up the telephone and punched in a number. ''Nancy, ask Diamond Don's assistant to come in here. Yes, that's right.'' He replaced the receiver and sat back in his chair.

''Since when does Diamond Don work here?''

''Since he came out of retirement to become Chief Financial Officer.''

Parker absorbed this information. ''Good choice.''

''I thought so.''

Parker was beginning to suspect that things hadn't deteriorated as much as he'd expected. Diamond Don wouldn't let them.

He drew his first easy breath in several minutes.

''Jay?'' called a familiar female voice, and the door opened. ''Nancy said you wanted to see me?'' She took three steps into the room and stopped.

"Sorry, Abby." Jay stood. "There wasn't an easy way to tell you."

She glared at him. "I think a simple 'Abby, Parker's in my office' would have worked."

"Call it a flair for the dramatic. And now, though I think this is going to be one hell of an interesting conversation, I am going to leave you two alone."

Parker was barely aware of Jay's departure.

He was barely able to think or hear past the pounding in his ears.

Abby, sweet Abby, was standing only a few feet away from him, her arms crossed protectively over her basketball-sized belly.

CHAPTER ELEVEN

"YOU'RE pregnant."

"No, I drank too much eggnog at Christmas." After delivering that shot, Abby walked to the sofa in the conversation area, sat down and propped her feet on the coffee table.

"Nobody told me you were pregnant."

"Did you ask?"

"No, I didn't ask! It didn't occur to me to ask."

"Obviously. You walked off that beach, handed your pesky marriage problem off to your lawyers, and never gave me another thought."

"That's not true," Parker said in a low voice.

"Oh, right. I suppose you thought about me as you signed the divorce papers."

"Abby," he began, feeling uncertain how to proceed.

The woman sitting on the sofa bore little resemblance to the starry-eyed girl he'd swept off to Colombé. The only thing flashing in her eyes now was anger.

"You should have told me. *Someone* should have told me," he said, thinking of Jay. His brother was going to pay for this.

"When did anyone have the opportunity?" she asked. "You left me sobbing on the beach without a backward glance. Then you took off for El Bahar without speaking to me or your brother or your mother or anyone here at Laird. And when *they* tried to contact *you*, you were out in the field and couldn't be reached.''

Parker remembered leaving orders that he wouldn't take calls from his family. ''If you'd told Ian, he would have gotten word to me.''

''I didn't think you'd be interested and I've been humiliated enough, thank you very much.''

He was handling this all wrong. ''I—there aren't words to express my regret for what happened.''

''Oh, please try. I deserve some groveling.''

She was sweet and fresh and innocent and you spoiled it all in the name of business. Jay was right. ''Abby, I'm sorry.''

She gave him a direct look. ''Yes, you are.''

As he gazed at her, Parker realized that the Abby he'd known on Colombé was gone forever and he desperately wanted her back. ''I'd give anything to go back in time, but I can't. So I think the best way to handle this situation is to get married immediately.''

''Been there, done that.'' Abby struggled to her feet. ''And by the way, this isn't a situation, it's a baby.''

Parker stood, offering her his hand. She ignored it. ''We'll get the license this afternoon and I'm sure I can get a judge to waive the three-day waiting period.''

''I'm not marrying you.'' Abby walked toward the door. ''I've already married you. I didn't like it.''

She was being unnecessarily stubborn. ''I know you're angry and you have every right to be. But think of the baby.''

''I *am* thinking of the baby.''

''Abby!''

She turned at the door, her eyes cold.

''You have to marry me.''

"Why?"

"Because of the baby!"

She gave him a withering look and disappeared through the door. Parker ran after her, but Jay intercepted him.

"She won't marry me!" Parker was floored.

Jay raised an eyebrow. "And you're surprised?"

"But—but she's carrying my baby!"

"Are you sure it's your baby?"

A red mist covered Parker's vision. An instant later, his knuckles hurt and Jay was on the floor massaging his jaw.

But he was grinning.

Parker was horrified at his loss of control. "Jay, I'm sorry."

"No, this is a good thing." Jay hopped to his feet. "Now that I know you love her, I'll help you get her back."

Parker was stunned. "I love her?"

"Yeah, you do." Jay clapped him on the shoulders and guided him to the sofa where Abby had been sitting. "Kind of creeps up and hits you between the eyes, doesn't it?"

Parker nodded. "But *you* love her."

"Like a sister. And I mean that. Abby made me feel capable and important at a time when I needed to feel that way. And I have to tell you, looking out for her until you came to your senses made me grow up. That's when I hooked up with Lisa again." Jay sighed. "Now *that's* love."

"Jay?" Parker was still reeling. "I didn't know I loved her. You've got to believe me."

Jay cleared his throat. "I believe you. You were very convincing."

Parker held his head in his hands. ''She's never going to take me back.''

''Yes, she will. You've got a secret weapon.''

''What's that?''

Jay grinned. ''Me.''

''Tell your brother to stop sending me flowers.'' Abby dumped Parker's latest offering into Jay's wastebasket.

''Give the guy a chance, Abby.''

''He had his chance,'' she said, and lumbered out of the office.

Parker came out of the suite where he'd been eavesdropping. ''You see? Nothing is working.''

''And I've given you all my best material, too.'' Jay laced his fingers behind his head and stared at the ceiling. ''You remembered to send the pedicurist to her office, right?''

''Right.''

''Baby toys?''

''She sent them back. Same with the furniture.''

Jay shook his head. ''I wish you could take her to Colombé, but her delivery date's too near.''

''She won't even talk to me.'' Parker paced in front of the desk. ''And she's apparently not talking to anyone here. Nobody even knows we were married.''

''Diamond Don knows. He's not real happy with you.''

''That's an understatement.'' Diamond Don wouldn't even let him near Abby. Claimed he upset her and it wasn't good for the baby.

Parker felt like the scum of the earth, probably because he *was* the scum of the earth. ''It's my baby, too. I've got some rights here.''

''I hope you didn't tell her that.''

"No. I'm going to bring in the lawyers only as a last option."

"That's a relief." Jay rocked back so far in the chair, Parker was afraid he was going to fall over. "Have you talked to her any at all lately?"

"I caught her in the elevator a couple of days ago."

"And?"

"And she told me to leave her alone."

"Gee, I don't know." Jay sighed. "All you can do is keep telling her you love her and hope she softens."

Parker blinked.

The front legs of Jay's chair hit the floor. "Parker, you *have* told her you love her, haven't you?"

He frowned. "I don't know if I've actually said the words…but she knows how I feel."

"No, she doesn't!" Jay looked skyward and gestured with his hands. "I can't believe you! That's the number one rule with women. *You've got to say the words or nothing else counts.* Trust me. They want to hear the words. They want to hear you say 'I love you.' Any embellishment is okay, as long as the basics are there."

"Obviously, I don't have the advantage of your vast experience—"

"Put a sock in it, Parker." Jay picked up the phone and punched in two numbers. "Don, is she there?" Jay's eyes widened and he glanced toward Parker. "Well, where did she go?"

Parker froze. Something must have happened to Abby. He grabbed the phone from Jay. "Where's Abby?"

"She told me I wasn't to tell you," Diamond Don said in his gravelly voice.

"Tell me or I'll let every newspaper in the country know that your Texas-shaped diamond is a fake."

Jay gasped. ''It's *fake*?''

''Now, son, there's no need to be hasty...get it? Haste—y. In my opinion, Abby has been too *Haste-y.*''

Hasty? Haste. Parker exhaled. Abby had gone home to Haste. ''Thanks, Don.''

Parker hung up the telephone and ran across the room to his maps. ''Any idea where Haste, Texas, is?''

But Jay was grappling with something else. ''Diamond Don's diamond is *fake*?''

Parker grinned at his stunned brother. ''Don't tell.''

Haste, Texas, was a rural town with a courthouse on Main Street, a Dairy Queen and a Wal-Mart.

Parker hoped it had adequate medical facilities.

He had Abby's parents' address from her employment application and was currently driving up one tree-shaded street and down another in search of the correct tree-shaded street. Her parents lived on Sycamore Drive and he'd already passed Oak, Maple, Elm, Spruce, Ash and Magnolia.

Just how many other kinds of trees were there?

Sweet Gum, Pine, Aspen. And there at the end was Sycamore.

Parker found the house, a two-story, white frame with a porch. He stopped the car, ran up the front steps and pounded on the door, but no one answered.

Parker was filled with panic. What if Abby had had an accident while driving here? Or car trouble? What if she was stranded on the side of the road somewhere?

The door opened and a man with Abby's blue eyes stared at him.

Parker gulped air. ''I'm Parker Laird, the father of your grandchild.''

The man stared at him, taking his measure. Parker straightened and tried to slow his breathing.

''Well, I suppose with credentials like that, you'd best come in.'' He held open the screen door. ''I'm Bob Monroe. You caught me up in the attic.''

''How do you do, sir.''

Mr. Monroe gave him a look. ''It's been a very interesting day.''

''Abby didn't tell you about the baby, did she?''

''Nooo.'' Mr. Monroe led Parker into the den and pointed to a chair upholstered in a plaid fabric.

''We *were* married,'' Parker assured him. ''Briefly.''

''Long enough, it appears.''

Parker felt his face heat, something that hadn't happened since he was a boy. ''I've been overseas. I didn't know about the baby.''

''You said you *were* married.''

''And I want to be again, but Abby won't marry me.''

''Why not?''

''Because I was an idiot.''

Mr. Monroe nodded. ''Abby's a fairly good judge of character.''

''Mr. Monroe, if I could just talk with her, I think I could straighten everything out.''

''She's not here. She's at the hospital, fixin' to have the baby.''

Parker shot to his feet. ''Where's the hospital?''

''You don't need to rush over there. Her mother's with her. These first babies take hours to be born.'' Mr. Monroe stood. ''You might as well help me get the crib out of the attic.''

It took all his negotiating skills to pry the location of the hospital out of Mr. Monroe. But first, Parker stopped by the courthouse on Main Street and explained the situation to a sympathetic judge, who issued a marriage license and agreed to follow him to the hospital.

And there in a labor room with dancing yellow ducks on the walls, he found Abby and her mother.

"Abby! Are you all right?"

She was lying on her left side, a fetal monitor strapped to her abdomen. "Diamond Don is a traitor."

"Diamond Don is a good and wise man."

"Unlike you."

"Abby—"

Abby's mother pushed him aside. "She's having a contraction. She needs to concentrate on her breathing. Deep cleansing breath, Abby."

Abby responded, wincing when the contraction was at its peak.

"You must be Parker," her mother said to him when the contraction was over.

He nodded.

"I'll leave you two alone, then."

"Mother!"

But Abby's mother gave her a significant look and left the room.

"Great, now you've run off my coach."

"We've got to talk."

"So start talking. You've got about two minutes before the next contraction."

"Please, marry me, Abby." He remembered what Jay had said. "I love you."

Instead of going all mushy, Abby glared at him. "No, you don't. You're just saying that so I'll marry yo—'' She broke off and started breathing, then gasping.

Parker held her hand, feeling utterly useless.

Sweat beaded on Abby's face. ''They're coming closer together.''

''Abby, I've got a judge and a license. Please marry me before the baby is born.'' He tried again. ''I love you. I loved you on Colombé, but I didn't know it. I'd never felt that way before. Something happened on the island. It's true, I'd intended to keep you there until Jay left for El Bahar. I didn't have to marry you. But I did. And it was because I was in love with you.''

''No.'' She winced. ''Get my mother!''

The ''I love you'' wasn't working. Parker didn't know what else to do or say.

''I'm here, honey.'' Mrs. Monroe sent an apologetic look toward Parker. ''Why don't you listen to him?''

Abby was gripped by another contraction. ''He only wants to marry me because of the baby!'' she wailed.

''I'd want to marry you even without the baby!'' Parker shouted in exasperation. ''It's just because of the baby that I want to get married *now*.''

She was doing her breathing, so he wasn't even sure she heard him.

''You'd marry me even without the baby?''

''Yes,'' Parker said simply, then added, ''I love you.''

A luminous smile transformed Abby's face. ''He loves me.''

Mrs. Monroe smoothed her hair. ''Yes, sweetie, I think he does.''

''That's what I've been saying!''

"I love him, too." She looked at Parker. "I love you, too." She squeezed his hand as another contraction started.

"I'll get the judge," Parker said when it was over.

He found the man in the waiting room with Abby's father and brought them both back to the labor room.

"I called the doctor, as well," her mother said as a green-gowned man entered.

Parker took Abby's hand.

"Dearly beloved, we are gathered here—"

"How far apart are the contractions?"

"—to join Abigail and Parker—"

"Can you tell me when one is starting?"

"—in the bonds of holy matrimony—"

"—dilated to nine centimeters—"

"It is an honorable estate—"

"Tell delivery we're on our way."

The nurse raised the sides of the bed and Parker motioned for the judge to hurry. Abby moaned.

"—show just cause why they should not—"

"Remember your breathing! Don't push!"

"—forever hold his peace—"

"If you're going into the delivery room, you'll have to change into scrubs."

"Do you, Parker—"

"I do!"

"Don't push yet!"

"Do you, Abigail—"

"Ye-esssss!"

"We're rolling."

"Then by the power of the authority invested in me by the State of Texas—"

"I have to push!"

"I pronounce you husband and wife."

Parker kissed Abby on the forehead and ran to put on a hospital gown.

And twenty-five minutes later, Elizabeth Jayne Laird greeted her parents.

EPILOGUE

"ISN'T she beautiful?" Abby cooed to the little bundle in her arms.

"Not as beautiful as her mother," Parker said. At Abby's raised eyebrow, he added, "Yet."

Abby smiled down at Elizabeth, enjoying the fact that Parker was still on shaky ground with the two of them—and that he was aware of it.

A beam from the evening sun shone through the hospital room window.

"Is that too bright for her eyes?" Parker asked. "Shall I adjust the blinds?"

"Maybe a little," Abby directed.

Parker Laird waiting on her. Who'd have thought it?

For that matter, who'd have thought that she'd marry him not once, but twice, and was now holding his daughter in her arms?

Life could sure take some strange turns.

The evening sun reminded Abby of their first wedding. For so long the thought of it had brought only pain. Now she found some of the happiness she'd felt that day returning. "Did you really mean what you said about marrying me even without the baby?" she asked.

"Yes." Perhaps sensing that a single-word declaration wouldn't be enough, Parker drew a chair close to the bed. He sat, bending close to the baby, then pressing his lips on her forehead. "But I'm awfully glad she's here," he whispered. "She was conceived on Colombé, just as my love was."

Parker raised his head and met Abby's teary gaze. "But I didn't know about her then, and I didn't recognize that what I felt for you was love then. Both took nine months to grow."

Abby swallowed. "But why did you leave?"

"Your face." He closed his eyes briefly. "The look on your face when Jay said all those things. They were true, but they weren't true. I *did* take you to Kitt's house after Jay told me he loved you, but I didn't think he truly loved you. I convinced myself that he would hurt you. This way, you got a vacation and I got a manager for the El Bahar project."

"But why did you marry me?"

"I'd never felt the way I felt when we were together on the island. All I could think of was keeping that feeling forever. Jay made me realize how arrogantly selfish I'd been." His eyes turned bleak. "You were crying...he was holding you...and I remember thinking that he must have loved you after all."

"So you left."

Parker shook his head. "I tried to put things back the way they'd been and give him the chance to marry you."

"Did it ever occur to you to *ask* me if I wanted to marry Jay?"

"No."

Abby gave him a fondly exasperated smile. "I see that we're going to have to work on communication in this relationship."

Half smiling, Parker ran his finger over the baby's fuzzy head. "I've really wrecked your life, haven't I?"

"How can you say that?"

"Your classes—"

"I can still go to school. *You* can baby-sit."

He grinned. "I'll have time, too. You know, Jay didn't do a half bad job while I was gone."

"Jay did a fantastic job, and you know it."

"Good enough—good enough for me to turn over some of the responsibility for running the company to him."

"Oh, did you tell him that?"

Smiling ruefully, Parker rubbed the spot between his eyebrows. "Actually, he told me. But he's right. We don't agree on methods, but we do agree on goals. Which reminds me—I believe my wife likes to travel."

Abby looked down at her daughter. "I think your wife is going to be busy for a while."

"My wife *will* have a honeymoon," he pronounced, sounding just like the old Parker. "To…Italy. We'll take Elizabeth with us." He looked at her, obviously expecting her to smile and tell him how wonderful he was.

She didn't. "Did you *ask* if your wife wanted a honeymoon? Did you *ask* if she wanted to drag a baby to Italy?"

He looked abashed. "No, but I thought you'd want a honeymoon."

"I do." Abby tilted her chin up. "I want to go to Colombé."

A peculiar expression crossed Parker's face.

"What happened?" she asked, sudden dread spoiling her happiness. "Something bad happened between you and Mr. Ramsdell, didn't it? Now we can't visit the island, can we?"

Parker sat back in the chair and crossed his arms,

looking incredibly self-satisfied. "We can go there whenever we want. I bought it. For you."

"You bought the whole island?"

"I bought the house—the island came with it."

The baby stirred as Abby scrambled for something to say. "No one has ever given me an island before."

Parker leaned forward and pulled the receiving blanket away from Elizabeth's cheek. "No one has ever given me a child before."

He touched the baby's cheek and she turned her face toward him. The wonder in his smile brought tears to Abby's eyes and contentment to her heart. "I guess there really is island magic," she whispered.

Parker smiled up at her. "I call it love."